EAA *Aviation* FOUNDATION

Compiled and prepared
by Paul Poberezny
and S.H. "Wes" Schmid

Contents

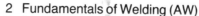

OVERSIZE

KEY
(AW) — Aircraft Welding - Navy Training Courses, 1950 Edition
(SA) — Sport Aviation (EAA)
(PE) — Product Engineering, October 1940
(USAF) — U.S. Air Force General Manual for Structural Repair, Third Edition, October 1963
(AD) — Aircraft Design Through Service Experience (CAA Technical Manual No. 103, September 1953)
(AB) — The Techniques of Aircraft Building
(LPW) — Light Plane World, April 1985

Copyright 1991 by the Experimental Aircraft Association, Inc.
All rights reserved.
PUBLISHED JUNE 1994
Printed by Times Printing Company, Inc., Random Lake, WI

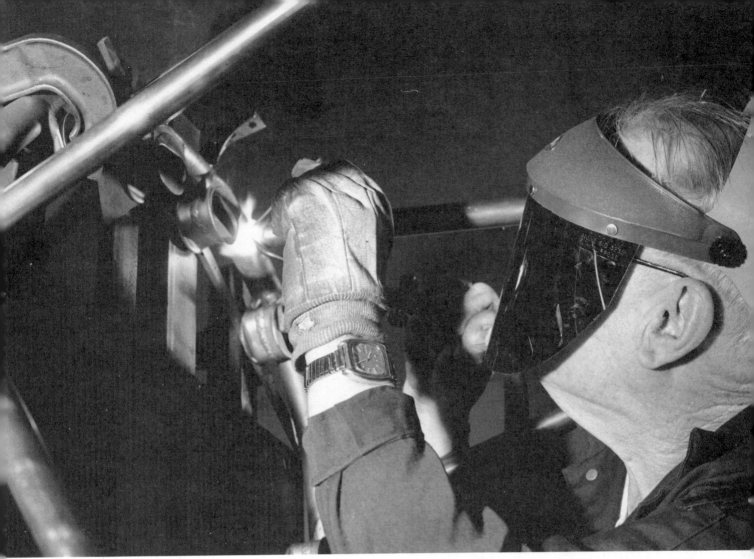

Always wear proper welding goggles or face shield when welding, as well as protective clothing to prevent burns from sparks.

Fundamentals Of Welding

Aircraft Maintenance And Welding

A knowledge of aircraft welding is of primary importance to the aircraft builder.

The repair of welded aircraft structures may be divided into two general classifications — the repair of structural welded parts and assemblies, and the repair of nonstructural parts and assemblies. The former category includes welded steel fuselages, landing gears, tail surfaces, and engine mounts, while nonstructural parts refer to aluminum alloy cowlings, fuel tanks, and exhaust stacks and manifolds which are fabricated from steel of the stainless or heat-resistant types.

Welding is used not only for the repairs mentioned in the preceding paragraph, but also for fabricating jigs and fixtures for repair and for repairing heavy machinery. In the aviation structural mechanic schools, instruction predominates in the oxyacetylene method, as this process is employed in the welding of the majority

of aircraft metals. A brief comparison of the different welding processes will provide a background for the intensive study of oxyacetylene welding.

Welding Defined

In general, welding consist of the controlled melting or fusing of adjacent edges or surfaces of metals so that the molten portions flow together into a common mass of metal. Upon cooling, the fused portions are united into a castlike structure which binds or joins the surrounding areas of metal.

Welding may be divided into two general classifications — PRESSURE and NONPRESSURE. In pressure welding, the surfaces to be joined are heated until they are in a plastic or semimolten stage, and are then joined by applied forces. Examples of this class of welding are FORGE, SPOT, and RESISTANCE welding. In nonpressure welding, the surfaces to be fused are brought to a molten state and caused to flow together. In this latter class may be found THERMIT, ELECTRIC ARC, OXYHYDROGEN, and OXYACETYLENE welding.

Welding Processes Defined

The following brief explanations of the different welding processes are taken from the tenth edition of the *Welding Encyclopedia.*

FORGE WELDING is a process of welding metals in the plastic state by means of manual or mechanical hammering. This process includes blacksmith welding, hammer welding, and roll welding.

SPOT WELDING is a resistance welding process wherein the weld is made in one or more spots by the localization of the electric current between contact points.

RESISTANCE WELDING is a pressure welding process wherein the welding heat is obtained by passing an electric current across the resistance set up between the contact area to be welded.

THERMIT WELDING is the process of heating aluminum and iron oxide to approximately 5,000° F. These molten oxides are applied to the metal to be welded at which time a chemical reaction fuses the filler metal to the preheated base metal.

ARC WELDING is the concentration of the heat in an electric circuit at an air or gas gap for the purpose of raising metals to be joined to a melting temperature.

OXYHYDROGEN WELDING is accomplished by using a torch flame to heat the metal. The flame is produced by the combustion of a mixture of one volume of oxygen with four volumes of hydrogen in order to prevent oxidation of the metal. The temperature of the flame is about 4,300° F.

OXYACETYLENE WELDING is a process of fusing metals together with heat produced by the combustion of oxygen and acetylene. The chemical union of these two gases produce the hottest flame known to man — about 6,300° F. The oxyacetylene process is widely used in aircraft welding because of this high temperature, and because the flame is easy to regulate. Oxygen and acetylene are easy to produce in large quantities and can be transported safely when properly confined.

Properties Of Metals

Because of the relatively low safety factor in airplane structures, all metals used in aircraft construction will possess greater strength in proportion to weight. They will also possess other properties in widely different degrees because of the varying uses to which they are put. A general knowledge of the properties of metals — especially as they are affected by welding will enable a builder to make a repair acceptable in all respects because most of the original qualities of the metal are left intact.

Some of the properties of metals, by which their adaptability to aircraft may be evaluated, are:

1. Strength.
2. Elasticity.
3. Ductility.
4. Toughness.
5. Fatigue resistance.
6. Durability.
7. Hardness.
8. Ease of fabrication.

Aircraft metals must have a high strength-to-weight ratio. The aircraft structure, exclusive of engine, tanks, etc., represents from 25 to 35 percent of the total weight of the craft, despite every refinement in design. It is obvious that the weight of every separate part must be kept to a minimum.

The advantage of one aircraft material over another increases approximately as the square of the strength-

Upper fuselage longerons securely clamped to vertical side assembly jig for tack welding of cross members. Accuracy cannot be overemphasized - and dimensions and alignment should be checked constantly.

to-weight ratio. It is this characteristic that makes aluminum so valuable, since it is only one-third as heavy as steel. High-strength steel alloys also possess a high strength-to-weight ratio, but they are rather difficult to form into the thin cross sections which must be used to attain a low weight comparable to that of aluminum.

Fatigue Resistance

Another factor which is particularly important in the metals used in aircraft construction is fatigue resistance. Aircraft structures must withstand repeatedly applied loads or reversals of loading, and are continually subjected to severe vibration. To avoid failure of aircraft structures, welds on structural parts must be made in such a way as to maintain the fatigue resistance of the parts.

Relation Of Qualities

The qualities of elasticity, ductility, toughness, and hardness are closely related, and an increase in one quality may often be gained only at the expense of a reduction in one or more of the other properties. For example, hardened carbon steel is less elastic and ductile than the same steel in a tempered condition. Stainless steel, however, is likely to have most of these qualities to a high degree.

Durability

It is desirable that the material used in an airplane be affected as little as possible by changes in climatic conditions, or unfavorable storage facilities. Resistance to the corrosive action of moisture or salt spray is a highly important quality.

Examples of a metal selected for its durability are alclad sheet and stainless steel. Alclad sheet is a light metal used for airplane skin because of its corrosion

Figure 1.—Steel L rail used as both heat conductor and jig for a light-gage T-joint.

resisting qualities, and stainless steel is used in exhaust collectors because of its heat-resisting properties.

Since heat affects the qualities of resistance to corrosion of all aircraft metals, welding must be performed in such manner as to avoid seriously impairing these qualities. It is also necessary that these qualities be restored in some cases by the proper heat treatment when the welding is completed.

Aircraft materials must obviously be easy to bend or to form. For this reason, aluminum and its alloys is used for cowl rings; skin; on fuselage and wings and also for formed or extruded ribs, spars, or bulkheads. Chrome molybdenum steel is also quite readily formed into desired shapes and is used for structural members where great strength is required. Metal for aircraft use must also be rather easily riveted or welded since speed and ease of assembly are important factors in their usefulness.

Aircraft Metals

Some of the metals used in aircraft which require welding in fabrication or repair are CARBON STEEL, CHROME MOLYBDENUM STEELS, AND STAINLESS STEELS. There are other metals which are more infrequently used and which do not require welding in their repair, that can be listed as aircraft metals. These are brass, copper, and bronze.

Carbon Steel

Although aluminum, with its alloys, is the metal used to the greatest extent in aircraft construction, steel and its alloys still comprise about 20 percent of the structural weight of the airplane. Carbon steels were at one time the only metals of this type used for structural parts. At present, these steels have been largely superseded by chrome molybdenum steel.

All steels contain carbon in varying amounts, but only those containing no other alloying element are referred to as carbon steel. The steels which are generally used for parts fabricated by welding are those containing not more than 0.30 percent carbon. Due to the fact that molten steel has a great affinity for carbon, extreme care must be exercised during welding to avoid change in its content.

Those steels containing less than 0.30 percent carbon are known as LOW CARBON STEELS. They are comparatively elastic, tough, and ductile, but are not exceptionally hard or strong. They are easily welded by all processes, and the resulting welds or joints are of extremely high quality.

MEDIUM CARBON STEELS — containing from 0.30 to 0.50 percent carbon — are hardened as a result of the increased amount of carbon present. They can be welded fairly easily by the oxyacetylene process. In some cases, preheating may be necessary, in addition to heat treatment after welding, to produce the desired weld quality. This is especially true for steels containing over 0.40 percent carbon.

HIGH CARBON STEELS, containing from 0.50 to

Table 1. — Expansion Of Metals

Metal	Coefficient of expansion (inches)	Melting point
Aluminum	0.00001280	1,220
Copper	.00000923	1,981
Low carbon steel	.00000630	2,714
Cast iron	.00000590	2,250

0.90 percent carbon, are harder and more brittle because of the higher carbon content. These steels are generally heat treated because they are used for tools where hardness and strength are the desired qualities. The welding will affect the heat treatment and produce a joint of different properties than those possessed by the original metal. Care should be taken to prevent overheating of these parts, and the weld should be completed as quickly as possible. Materials to be welded are often preheated to speed up the welding process.

Chrome Molybdenum Steel

Chrome molybdenum steel has almost completely replaced carbon steel in such applications as fuselage tubing, landing gear struts, and other structural parts because of its high strength, ease of forming, and adaptability to welding.

A much-used series of chrome molybdenum steel has a carbon range of 0.25 to 0.55 percent, molybdenum 0.15 to 0.25 percent, and chromium 0.50 to 1.10 percent. These steels, when suitably heat treated, are deep hardening, easily machined, and readily welded by either gas or electric methods.

Because chrome molybdenum steel is thin walled, it air-hardens readily, resulting in high tensile strength and low ductility. In welding it, consideration must be given to expansion and contraction, and to avoiding undue stress on the hot metal.

Stainless Steels — Chrome Nickel Alloys

Alloys in this classification contain sufficient nickel and manganese, in addition to the chromium (with or without small amounts of other metals), to maintain an essentially austenitic condition. In other words, stainless steels have such a grain structure at ordinary temperatures that they possess low heat conductivity, comparatively high coefficient of expansion, nonmagnetic properties, and satisfactory toughness.

All stainless steels, except those stabilized by colombium or titanium, when exposed to temperatures of 700° to 1,500° F., will show an accumulation of carbides at the grain boundaries. This is known as CARBIDE PRECIPITATION and is found in stainless steel that has been held in this temperature range. It is found also in lines approximately parallel to the weld bead up to a quarter-inch distance even in stainless steel plates that have been properly heat-treated after welding. This is the result of the heat of the welding operation,

and is evidence that the plate metal in that narrow zone has been heated to a temperature range wherein carbide precipitation can take place.

Stainless steels containing colombium, titanium, or molybdenum are "stabilized" (to dissolve precipitated carbides and to prevent intergranular corrosion) by heating to 1,550°-1,625° F., for from 2 to 4 hours, and then quenching, as in annealing. This is done after the welding operation has been completed.

Stainless steel will conduct heat only about 40 percent as fast as mild steel, but its coefficient of expansion is about 50 percent greater than mild steel. Since the distribution of heat from the acetylene flame is wider than that obtained from arc methods, it is desirable to use chill blocks to absorb the heat when welding with gas. Since most of the stainless steel used in aircraft applications is one-sixteenth inch or less, extensive use of jigs and clamps will be necessary to control buckling and warping.

Expansion And Contraction

The principles of EXPANSION AND CONTRACTION of metals is based upon facts which are easily understood. When metal is heated, it expands appreciably in all its dimensions. When metal cools, it becomes reduced in size — it contracts.

Steel rails in a railroad track show clearly the effect

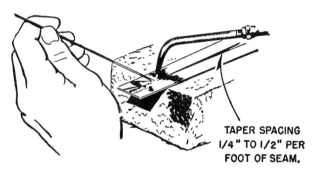

TAPER SPACING
1/4" TO 1/2" PER
FOOT OF SEAM.

Figure 2.—Allowance for contraction.

of changes in temperature upon metal. Summer heat expands the rails until the ends of all sections of the rails are in contact; low winter temperatures cause the rails to contract until there is a sizeable gap between the ends.

The extreme range in temperature to which welded parts are subjected creates a serious problem for the welder. The forces of expansion and contraction cannot be eliminated or mechanically controlled. If the welder is to produce satisfactory welds, he must have a knowledge of the amount of expansion and contraction encountered in the different metals he must weld. He must also have a knowledge of the effects these forces have on different thicknesses and compositions of metals, and of the steps which can be taken to counteract or compensate for these forces.

The rate of expansion of different metals is constant and the amount of expansion varies directly with the temperature. Scientists call the rate of expansion "CO EFFICIENT OF EXPANSION." This term refers to the

5

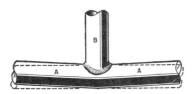

Figure 3. — Effect of improper welding technique on tubular structures.

amount that a unit length of metal will increase in length if the temperature is raised 1° F. The amount that a given metal will expand can be readily calculated from the figures given in table 1. For example, if a 10-foot low carbon rod is heated from 70° to 2,700°, the increase in length is equal to 0.00000630 x 2630 x 120, which equals 1.99 inches.

Not only is the amount of expansion different for each metal, but the rate at which the heat is conducted is also quite different for each of the metals which must be welded. There are other factors which influence the amount of expansion or contraction in a welded structure or part, such as thickness of the part, the speed of welding, and the method of clamping. If the parts being welded are free to expand in all directions, the welder will usually have little trouble, as the parts will expand equally, and in cooling can return to their original dimensions. In general, more trouble is due to contraction while the metal is cooling. The weld metal is so soft that expansion is taken care of by a thickening

Fuselage sides securely held in place top and bottom while cross members are cut, filed to shape, and fitted for tack welding.

or upsetting of the metal. If the welder understands what effects expansion and contraction will have upon a particular job, he should generally be able to devise some means of compensating for these forces.

Effect On Sheet Metal

The effect of expansion and contraction due to the heat from the welding flame on thin sheet (one-eighth inch or less in thickness) is a tendency to develop buckling or warping. This buckling or warping is a result of the greater amount of surface area in proportion to the weight. The welding heat spreads rapidly, and the metal cools very quickly when the source of heat is removed.

Expansion on thin sheets may be controlled somewhat by tacking along the joint, but the most effective means of alleviating the warping is to remove some of the heat from the metal near the weld. Heavy pieces of metal, known as CHILL BARS, may be placed on either side of the seam, as shown in figure 1. Welding jigs utilize this same principle of removing the heat from the base metal.

Long seams (over 10 to 12 inches) have a tendency to draw together as the weld progresses. The spot being welded is melted so rapidly that most of the expansion is taken care of in the molten metal. As the metal cools, it contracts and tends to draw the seam together. This can be overcome by setting up the parts to be welded with an increased allowance at the far end, which varies according to the metal used, and its thickness. This allowance per foot of seam is generally one-fourth to three-eighths inch per foot of seam for steel. This principle is illustrated in figure 2.

Sheet metal under one-sixteenth inch in thickness is best handled by flanging the edges, tack-welding at intervals along the seam, and then welding.

Plates

There is less tendency to warp and buckle when plate (over ⅛-inch stock) is welded, because of the greater proportion of metal to surface area, which limits the flow of heat from the welded area. However, it is advisable to allow the same amount of contraction along a long straight seam as was allowed on thin sheet. Preheating will help to prevent cracks caused by uneven expansion and contraction.

Tubular Structures

A welded tubular structure will have terrific stresses set up by the welding, if preventive measures are not taken. When welding two members of a **T**-joint, as shown in figure 3, tube (A) tends to draw up. This is due to the fact that most of the expansion is taken care of in the molten metal, but as the weld cools, the base metal contracts beyond its original shape.

Buckling can be relieved by preheating before the welding operation begins. Contraction still takes place at the weld, but there is also shrinking in the rest of the structure at approximately the same rate. Internal stress at the weld is thereby relieved.

Introduction To Oxyacetylene Welding

Equipment

The amount of equipment required for successful oxyacetylene welding operations is considerable. A portable unit, illustrated in figure 4, is generally fastened on a hand truck so that it may be moved from place to place as needed. It consists of the following elements: TWO CYLINDERS, one containing oxygen and the other acetylene; a WELDING TORCH with

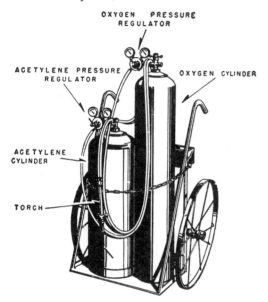

Figure 4. — Portable oxyacetylene welding equipment.

necessary tips and mixing head; lengths of green or black HOSE FOR OXYGEN, and red or maroon HOSE FOR ACETYLENE; and miscellaneous equipment such as GOGGLES, FRICTION LIGHTER, WRENCH, and FIRE EXTINGUISHER.

Oxygen

OXYGEN, an odorless, tasteless, colorless gas, is needed in welding to mix with the acetylene and cause the gas to burn at a temperature high enough to melt the metal being welded. Oxygen itself does not burn — IT SUPPORTS COMBUSTION. The oxygen in the air is that element causing any inflammable substance to burn.

Air is about one-fifth oxygen, the rest being nitrogen with a small percentage of rarer gases such as argon, neon, and helium. These gases in the air are simply a scrambled mixture, with no chemical union, although special machinery and processes are required to separate them and to transform air from a gas into a liquid.

When this separation and transformation occurs,

the liquid air obtained is an extremely cold mixture of liquid oxygen and liquid nitrogen. Oxygen is isolated from the nitrogen by a process known as RECTIFICATION, which delivers high purity oxygen to a storage holder from which it is compressed into steel cylinders for shipment.

Oxygen Cylinders

Typical OXYGEN CYLINDERS, such as shown in figure 5, are made of seamless drawn steel. A typical oxygen cylinder for welding and cutting operations is approximately 9 inches in diameter and 51 inches long, holding 200 cubic feet of oxygen at 1,800 pounds of pressure.

The technical oxygen cylinder identifying color marking is black with a 6-inch dark-green band at the

Figure 5. — The oxygen cylinder valve with cross-sectional view shown in inset.

top. The top of each cylinder is equipped with a HIGH-PRESSURE VALVE which controls the flow of oxygen. This valve has a double seat to insure a tight seal when fully opened or fully closed.

The iron SAFETY CAP provided to protect the valve should always be in place when the cylinder is not in use.

Oxygen cylinders are tested to withstand twice the normally required pressure. In addition, a safety device is fitted to the valve of each cylinder to relieve the oxygen in case the pressure in the cylinder should get out of hand. When the temperature reaches 208° to 220° F., and pressure builds up between 2,700 and 3,000 pounds, the safety device breaks and releases the oxygen, thus preventing any dangerous pressures within the cylinder. This safety device consists of a thin, frangible metal alloy disc and a fusible plug arrangement.

Acetylene

ACETYLENE GAS, a compound of carbon and hydrogen, is the fuel used in the production of the high temperature (5,700° to 6,300° F.) oxy-acetylene flame. It is a colorless gas with a disagreeable odor derived from the calcium carbide from which it is made. When carbide is dropped into water, bubbles of acetylene gas arise which, if lighted, burn with a very smoky flame.

MIXED WITH AIR OR OXYGEN, ACETYLENE FORMS AN EXTREMELY EXPLOSIVE MIXTURE. A spark introduced into such a mixture will cause almost instantaneous combustion and a violent explosion. The range of explosive mixtures varies from 3 percent acetylene and 97 percent air to 82 percent acetylene and 18 percent air.

Acetylene Cylinders

Typical acetylene cylinders are constructed of a seamless shell with welded ends and are built to hold 225 cubic feet of gas. They are approximately 12 inches in diameter and 36 inches long. The color marking for acetylene cylinders is yellow. (Navy).

Acetylene cylinders are quite different in construction from oxygen cylinders. Because free acetylene should not be compressed above 15 p.s.i., the steel cylinders are packed with a porous material. The fine

FILLER PLUGS
soft-lead centers
act as fusible safety
plugs.

Figure 6. — Attaching the regulator unit to an acetylene cylinder.

pores of this material are then filled with acetone, a liquid chemical capable of dissolving or absorbing many times its own volume of acetylene.

The cylinders are provided with a valve having a threaded outlet connection for attaching an ACETYLENE REGULATOR. SAFETY FUSE PLUGS are attached at each end of the cylinders to meet any fire emergencies (see fig. 6). These safety plugs melt at a temperature of 212° F., allowing the gas to escape from the overheated cylinder.

Regulators

REGULATORS perform the important functions of reducing the pressure and controlling the amount of gas flowing from the cylinders to the welding torch. They may be adjusted to reduce the cylinder pressure to any desired point and maintain such pressure constant without further attention.

In order to maintain constant torch pressure — without regard to cylinder pressure — regulators must have a sensitive regulating mechanism in addition to a reducing valve.

A regulator has a union nipple for attaching to the cylinder and an outlet connection for the hose leading to the torch. These devices are equipped with two pressure gages — a HIGH-PRESSURE GAGE showing the pressure of gas in the cylinder, and a LOW-PRESSURE GAGE indicating the pressure of gases flowing to the torch. The working pressure is adjusted by means of a handscrew. Changes in pressure are made simply by turning the handle until the desired pressure is registered.

The high-pressure gage on the OXYGEN REGULATOR is graduated in pounds per square inch from zero to 2,000, and the low-pressure gage is usually graduated in pounds per square inch from zero to 100 or from zero to 150.

ACETYLENE REGULATORS are not made to withstand the high pressures common to the oxygen regulators, although the two are practically identical in design. On an acetylene regulator, the high-pressure gage is capable of registering pressure up to 50 p.s.i., and the working gage may also register as high as 50 p.s.i.

An OXYGEN REGULATOR can be either a two-stage or a single-stage type. The two-stage type is preferable when using a portable welding outfit. The single-stage type may be used at individual welding stations where the stationary type of equipment is installed.

The TWO-STAGE OXYGEN REGULATOR has a dual action. When the cylinder valve is opened, the regulator automatically reduces the initial cylinder pressure to about 200 p. s. i. Then the pressure-adjusting screw is turned to the right (clockwise) until the required pressure is shown on the working pressure gage.

A typical two-stage oxygen regulator is shown in figure 7. This type of regulator has two independent diaphragms and stem-type valve assemblies, which render operation extremely efficient. The first stage extra-heavy diaphragm, with its heavy springs, reduces the full cylinder pressure of 2,000 p. s. i. to about 250 pounds. The first stage is wholly automatic and nonadjustable. The second stage differs in that it has a larger diaphragm and lighter springs. A pressure-adjusting screw makes it possible to obtain any desired working pressure.

This second stage is not required to carry the full cylinder pressure load, but functions within a comparatively narrow range. Dual arrangement of valves and diaphragms insures much more constant delivery pressure adjustment than is possible with single-stage regulators.

Welding Torches

WELDING TORCHES are devices producing an oxyacetylene flame under conditions of complete control as to flame size, characteristics, and ease of applications. Welding torches may vary in design, but all types have the same fundamental characteristics.

Welding torches have a handle with two inlet connections for gases at one end, and each is equipped with a valve for control of the volume of gas passing through. Desired proportions of oxygen and acetylene

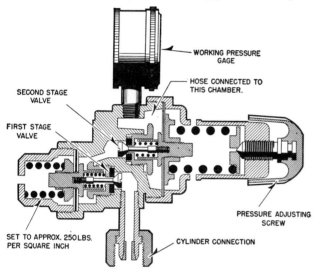

Figure 7. — Sectional view of typical two-stage oxygen regulator.

are thus allowed to pass through the torch and thoroughly mix before issuing from the tip or nozzle where the oxyacetylene flame is created by igniting the mixture.

There are two general types of oxyacetylene torches — the EQUAL or BALANCED-PRESSURE type, and the LOW-PRESSURE or INJECTOR type. The balanced-pressure torch is designed to operate under an acetylene pressure of 1 pound or more. Low-pressure, or injector-type, torches operate with a low acetylene pressure of not more than 1 pound per square inch.

In equal pressure torches, oxygen and acetylene are supplied at independent pressures to a MIXING CHAMBER, the construction of which depends upon the particular make of torch. In the injector-type torch, the oxygen at a comparatively high pressure sucks the acetylene into the mixing chamber where the two gases are thoroughly mixed and passed on to the tip.

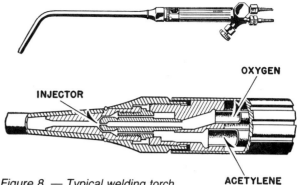

Figure 8. — Typical welding torch.

To understand the construction and operation of a welding torch, let us examine the typical type shown in figure 8. At the right of the illustrated unit is the REAR BODY which contains the hose connections and the inlet valves for oxygen and acetylene. Attached to the rear body is the HANDLE which is a brass tube with the front body set in the other end to form the terminal for the two smaller tubes inside the handle and to receive the INJECTOR located in the rear of the head.

Mixing takes place in the TORCH HEAD, the rear end of which is shown in cross-section attached to the handle in figure 8. The oxygen passes through the center of the INJECTOR NOZZLE. Surrounding the nozzle are a number of acetylene passageways. As oxygen passes through the small orifice of the injector nozzle, its velocity is increased and a suction is produced that draws acetylene in through the side openings. The passage through which the mixed gases then pass increases in diameter as the stem portion of the head is reached. This expansion insures thorough mixing of oxygen and acetylene, so the mixture issuing from the TORCH TIP will burn properly.

CUTTING TORCHES are so designed that the flame is fed from several small jets surrounding a central opening in the tip. The central opening — connected by an independent tube and valve to the oxygen supply — provides the jet of oxygen which does the cutting.

Torch Tips

TORCH TIPS deliver and control the final flow of gases. They are made of copper because it is an excellent conductor of heat, because it is non-corrosive, and because it has a low coefficient of expansion. The tips, being close to the work and therefore to the heat, must be able to dissipate heat quickly if the welding torch is to function properly.

For some types of torches, heads are available with either a one-piece drawn stem or a two-piece stem, the extra part consisting of a detachable tip. In either case, tips are fastened to the torch by means of a union nut so that the tip may be adjusted to any convenient angle.

Tip Sizes

There is no standard system for indicating the size of the opening in the torch tip, which determines the amount of heat available for welding. It is important

Table 2. — Torch Tip Sizes

Tip size (inches)	Tip drill size	Smith tip No.	Victor tip No.	Airco tip No.	Approximate thickness of steel sheet or plate
0.0200	76	----	-----	00	1/64-1/32
.0210	75	----	000	----	1/64-1/32
.0225	74	20	-----	----	1/64-1/32
.0250	72	----	-----	0	1/32-3/32
.0260	71	21	-----	----	1/64-3/64
.0280	70	----	00	----	1/64-3/64
.0310	68	22	-----	1	1/16-1/8
.0350	65	23	0	----	1/32-5/64
.0380	62	24	-----	2	3/32-5/32
.0400	60	----	1	----	3/64-3/32
.0420	58	25	-----	----	1/16-1/8
.0465	56	26	2	3	1/8-3/16
.0550	54	27	-----	4	5/32-7/32
.0595	53	----	3	----	1/8-3/16
.0635	52	28	-----	----	1/8-3/16
.0670	51	----	-----	5	3/16-5/16
.0700	50	29	-----	----	1/8-5/16
.0730	49	----	4	----	3/16-1/4
.0760	48	----	-----	6	1/4-3/8

that the correct tip be selected and used with the proper gas pressures if a job is to be satisfactorily welded. If too small a tip is used, the heat provided will not be adequate to secure penetration to the required depth. The use of too large a tip involves the danger of burning or overheating the metal.

Each manufacturer uses a different number system for the various sizes of tips provided. Some comparison of the tips supplied by various torch manufacturers can be had from a study of Table 2 which shows the diameter of the opening, the corresponding drill size, the numbers used by the various companies to designate different tips, and the size of metal for which the tip is adapted. This last item is approximate, as it is based on the tables provided by several companies. Furthermore, the size of tip required is affected not only by the thickness of the metal to be welded, but also by the heat conductivity of the metal.

The best rule to follow is to remember that the smaller numbers designate small gas passages, producing a small flame suitable for welding thin material, and the higher numbers denote comparatively larger gas passages and a large flame suitable for welding thicker metal.

Use of the correct size tip is not only instrumental in securing a sound weld with good penetration and even overlapping ripples, but also aids materially in eliminating backfires. Experience will enable the welder to automatically select the proper tip for any welding job. The following table is included principally for the information of the newcomer to aircraft welding, as a ready source of reference pending the acquisition of experience.

Tips are provided with protective dust caps which should be left on when the tips are not in use. Remove the dust cap before installing the tip and wipe the threads and seats clean so that no dust or foreign substances remain to prevent the tip from fitting tightly onto the torch head. Tips should be screwed on with the fingers and then tightened finally with the proper size open-end wrench. PLIERS SHOULD NEVER BE USED TO REMOVE OR TIGHTEN A TIP.

Frequent use of the torch will create a formation of carbon in the passages of the tip. Holding a torch closer than necessary to the molten puddle may permit particles of molten metal to pop into the tip. Clogged tubes and tips are indicated when greater pressure of the gases is necessary to produce the flame than is normally required for the size of tip being used, causing the flame to be split or distorted.

Tips that have become clogged from carbon deposits or by foreign matter should be properly cleaned out before use. Clean the tip, preferably with the proper size tip drill, or with a soft copper or brass wire. Fine steel wool may be used to remove the oxides from the outside of a tip.

Welding Flames

In welding with the oxyacetylene process, the source of heat is a flame. If the two gases which produce this flame — oxygen and acetylene — are brought together in the proper proportions, the flame conditions may be corrected for any welding operation.

Welding equipment is designed to enable the operator to produce a flame of the size and character best suited for the job at hand. For most metals, the supply of gas to the torch tip is adjusted so that there will be just enough of each gas to produce a balanced mixture. As a result, the flame produced will be NEUTRAL. There will be no unconsumed oxygen to oxidize the hot metal of the weld; neither will there be any unburned carbon (from the acetylene) to be absorbed by the hot metal.

Besides the neutral flame, there are two other basic flames that can be obtained from the oxyacetylene torch — CARBURIZING AND OXIDIZING. These flames can be created by changing the relative proportions of acetylene and oxygen. Changing the proportions of the gases directly affects the chemical characteristics of the flame, and in turn determines the action of the molten metal under the flame.

Neutral Flame

The NEUTRAL FLAME is the one best suited to the welding of most metals since it gives the hottest possible flame with no excess carbon or acetylene present. The neutral flame has a characteristic appearance, featured by two sharply defined zones. The INNER PORTION of the flame consists of a brilliant white cone from 1/16-inch to 3/4-inch long. Surrounding this is a larger cone, or "envelope flame," only faintly luminous and of a delicate bluish color.

In the neutral flame, two and one-half volumes of oxygen are required to burn one volume of acetylene. The air surrounding the flame supplies one and one-

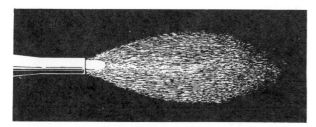

NEUTRAL FLAME
BALANCED MIXTURE. Brilliant white cone surrounded by larger "envelope flame" of pale blue color.

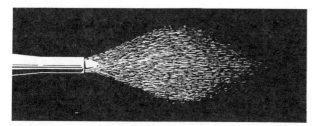

OXIDIZING FLAME
EXCESSIVE OXYGEN. Similar to neutral flame; shorter, neck-in, and acquires a purplish tinge.

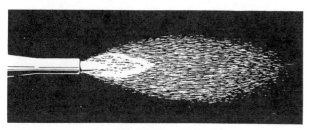

CARBURIZING FLAME
EXCESSIVE ACETYLENE. Three distinct zones. Brilliant white inner cone, whitish intermediate cone, and bluish outer envelope.

Figure 9. — Types of welding flames.

half volumes of oxygen, the remaining volume being supplied through the torch. Since the proportions of oxygen and acetylene supplied by the torch are equal or balanced, the flame produced by this mixture is called a NEUTRAL FLAME.

The neutral flame is of particular importance to the welder because it is used for such a wide variety of welding and cutting operations and because it serves as a basis of reference in making other flame adjustments. Therefore, one of the first duties of a welder should be to become perfectly familiar with the appearance and characteristics of the neutral oxyacetylene flame.

Carburizing Flame

A flame with an excess of acetylene is known as a REDUCING or CARBURIZING FLAME because the unburned carbon in the flame is readily absorbed by the molten metal, producing a brittle, carburized surface.

The carburizing flame consists of three easily recognizable zones instead of the two existing in the neutral flame. There is still a sharply defined inner cone and the bluish outer envelope, but between these — surrounding the inner cone — is an intermediate cone

of whitish color, as may be seen in figure 9. The length of this intermediate or excess acetylene cone may be taken as a measure of the amount of excess acetylene in the flame.

Oxidizing Flame

If there is an excess of oxygen in the flame mixture, the flame is known as an OXIDIZING FLAME. It has the general appearance of the neutral flame, but the inner cone is shorter, slightly pointed, and tinged with a bluish color.

A slightly oxidizing flame is used in bronze welding and bronze surfacing, while a more strongly oxidizing flame is used in fusion welding brass and bronze. An oxidizing flame can be recognized when welding ferrous metals by the numerous sparks which are thrown off as the metal melts and by the white foam or scum which forms on the surface. An oxidizing flame is harmful to ferrous metals and is carefully avoided on that account.

Flame Adjustment

In order to become familiar with the characteristics of the various types of flame and with the adjustments necessary to obtain them, light the welding torch with the acetylene valve wide open and the oxygen valve just slightly open. The acetylene will burn with a smoky yellow flame and will give off quantities of fine black soot.

Now open the torch oxygen valve slowly. The flame will gradually change in color from yellow to blue and will show the characteristics of the excess oxy-acetylene flame — that is, there will be three distinct parts to the flame; a brilliant but feathery-edged inner cone surrounded by a secondary cone, and a bluish outer envelope forming a third zone.

With most torches, there will still be a slight excess of acetylene when the oxygen and acetylene valves are wide open and the recommended pressures are

Rear wing strut fitting positioned in place prior to welding. Accuracy and alignment are critical.

being used. Now close the acetylene valve of the torch very slowly. It will be noticed that the secondary cone gets smaller until it finally disappears completely. Just at this point of complete disappearance the NEUTRAL FLAME is formed.

In order to see the effect of an excess of oxygen, close the acetylene valve still further. A change will be noted, although it is by no means as sharply defined as that between the neutral and excess acetylene flames. The entire flame will decrease in size and the inner cone will become much less sharply defined.

Adjusting To A Neutral Flame

Because of the difficulty of making a distinction between the EXCESS OXYGEN and NEUTRAL FLAMES, an adjustment of the flame to neutral should always be made from the excess acetylene side. Always adjust the flame first so that it shows the secondary cone characteristic of excess acetylene; then, increase the flow of oxygen until this secondary cone just disappears.

During the actual welding operations, where a neutral flame is essential, the flame should occasionally be checked to make certain it is neutral. This is accomplished by momentarily withdrawing the torch from the work and increasing the amount of acetylene until a distinctive feathery edge appears on the inner cone. The amount of acetylene is then slowly decreased until a well-defined cone, characteristic of the neutral flame, is formed.

With each size of tip, a neutral, oxidizing, or carburizing flame can be obtained. It is also possible to obtain a hard or soft flame by increasing or decreasing the pressure of both gases.

Hose

HOSE, made especially for the purpose, is used to connect the welding torch to the oxygen and acetylene cylinders. This hose is nonporous, durable, strong, and as lightweight as practicable. Welding hose is required to withstand a hydrostatic pressure test of 250 pounds per square inch.

Red or maroon hose is used for acetylene, and green or black for oxygen. In addition, the name of the gas is usually printed on the hose.

At each end, the hose is equipped with a connection by which it is attached to the regulator outlet and torch inlet. A connection with a right-hand thread is used on the oxygen hose, while a left-hand nut is used on the hose carrying acetylene. The left-hand acetylene nut is marked with a groove around its center, as illustrated in figure 10, while the right-hand nut for oxygen is plain. These connections are, in addition, marked STD. OXY, and STD. ACET.

OXYGEN   ACETYLENE

Figure 10. — Hose connections.

Lighters

Always use a FRICTION LIGHTER to ignite the torch. Never use matches. When lighting a torch with a match, the hand must be held so close that it may be burned when the gases ignite.

Filler Rods

Successful welding by the oxyacetylene process depends to a great extent upon the selection of the proper type of welding, or FILLER ROD. This material not only supplies necessary reinforcement to a weld area, but also adds desired properties to the finished weld or bead. By the selection of a suitable rod, either tensile strength or ductility can be secured in a weld, or both can be secured to a reasonably high degree. Similarly, rods can be selected which will help retain the desired amount of corrosion resistance. In some cases, a suitable rod with a lower melting point will eliminate possible cracks from expansion and contraction. In either case, these desired properties can be secured at the same time as a weld free of holes or oxides is developed.

Fin and rudder showing built-in rudder trim tab and receptacle for position light.

In the early days of welding, it was assumed that ideal results in welding could be obtained by using filler rods or strips practically identical to the base metal. It soon became evident, however, that the heat of welding developed a cast structure in the weld metal, which in some cases was entirely dissimilar to the original metal.

The rods used for welding of steel indicate some of the developments that came about as a result of the scientific study of the reaction of metals to the welding flame. The first step taken to improve welding rods for steel was to use a commercially pure iron, such as Swedish or Norway iron which contains 0.06 percent carbon or less. Without other elements, this rod produced a weld subject to corrosion.

In recent years, manufacturers have developed many types of rods — such as carbon steel rods and alloy steel rods — most of which contain materials that deoxidize the weld, and remove impurities without the use of a flux. Silicon and manganese are commonly used for this purpose. Similar improvements in nonferrous rods have made possible sound welds whose properties can be largely determined in advance. Copper-coated rods have been developed to prevent the corrosion of the rods themselves.

Welding rods may be classified as FERROUS or NONFERROUS. The ferrous rods include carbon and alloy steel rods as well as cast iron rods, while nonferrous rods include brazing and bronze rods, aluminum and aluminum alloy rods, copper rods, and silver rods. Usually, acetylene welding on ordinary steel with steel filler rods does not require the use of a flux. Welding of nonferrous metal with nonferrous rods, or the brazing of iron and steel with bronze rods, does require the use of flux. Stainless steel is also welded with the aid of a flux to prevent oxidation of the hot metal.

Ferrous Rods

While there are a number of rods available for the welding of steel and iron, the average welding shop may employ only a few since each manufacturer has some all-purpose rods which can be used in a number of applications. If there is any doubt as to the type of rod to use on a given metal, the suggestion of reputable manufacturers should be used.

Plain, low-carbon steel rods find the greatest all-round application in welding since they may be used not only for low-carbon steels, but also for welding chrome molybdenum tubing and welding stainless steel to chrome moly steel. Chrome molybdenum steel that is to be heat-treated is welded with a special high-test rod. Low-carbon steel rods generally have less than 0.06 percent carbon, but steel-alloy rods containing less than 0.15 percent carbon are also used for a general-purpose rod.

Another common type of ferrous rod is the high-test rod of higher carbon content for jobs where higher tensile strength is necessary. With this increase in tensile strength must come a decrease in ductility. The amount of manganese in these rods is increased so that the greater amount of carbon is not lost by reaction with

iron oxides, and to insure a clean, sound weld. All fittings and joints of carbon steel that must be heat-treated should be welded with high-carbon rods.

Corrosion-resistant steel should be welded with rods similar in alloy to the base metal. If the stainless steel is to be kept at its highest point of corrosion resistance, the welding rod must be of a type that contains small amounts of colombium, molybdenum, or titanium. These are used in stainless steel as stabilizing agents — that is, their presence in the steel prevents or restricts the precipitation of carbides at the grain boundaries, which action is the cause of lowered corrosion resistance.

Fluxes are usually employed on stainless steel to prevent oxidation. These fluxes are brushed on in the form of a thin paste, usually to the underside of the seam, although the rod may be dipped into the paste to help protect the bead. Stirring or puddling with the rod should be avoided.

Cast-iron rod is used for the welding of gray cast-iron maintenance tools and materials. The composition is similar to the base metal, and, in addition, rather large amounts of silicon are included. A typical specification includes 3.00 to 3.50 percent carbon, 3.00 to 3.50 percent silicon, 0.50 to 0.75 percent manganese, and 0.50 to 0.75 percent phosphorus.

Nonferrous Rods

Aircraft welding of nonferrous materials consists mostly of the welding of aluminum, and more rarely, of brazing or silver soldering. The rods used for these processes are of primary concern to the builder.

For ordinary shop practice, two types of ALUMINUM RODS are used — 2S and 43S. The 2S rod is of the same composition as 2S sheet or plate — that is, it consists of approximately 99 percent aluminum. The other rod used is 43S, available either as drawn or cast material, the cast rod being used only on cast aluminum. It is often referred to as the five-percent silicon rod, that being the percentage of silicon which it contains. Silicon produces four desirable reactions. It lowers the melting point; it makes the weld less brittle at welding temperatures; it reduces the amount of shrinkage while cooling; and it makes the weld more ductile. 43S rod is used for welding 53S and 51S and aluminum castings. Frequently, strips of base metal

Useful Tools

Don't throw away those stripped or worn out Phillips screwdrivers; they can be made into handy little tools.

The $3/16$ in. shank can be ground to a sharp point and used for marking metal, plexiglas, etc., or for lining up holes. The $1/4$ in. shank can be used to line up holes, or for temporary pins in fittings when assembling your aircraft. Round off or taper the end, and paint the handles to prevent their getting mixed up with the good screwdrivers.

Old aircraft bolts can be put to good use too, rather than be discarded. Cut off the head and taper the other end. These come in handy when aligning holes in fittings such as landing gears, wing struts, etc., or when replacing bolts. Simply lubricate the pin, insert the tapered end in the fitting hole, tap it in, and follow it through with the new bolt. This little tool can prevent damaged threads from a fitting which may be slightly misaligned.

by Wm. O. Alexander

are used for welding in order to make certain that the filler is of the same composition as the metal being welded.

Brazing rods are used for joining ferrous metals in those cases where it is desirable to join them without raising the temperature to the melting point. Brazing rods are composed of copper, tin, and zinc, a rod of typical composition contains 59 percent copper, 40 percent zinc, and 1 percent tin. Newer rods containing silicon produce greater strength and a more sound weld. Brazing is generally limited to the repair of machines and equipment used in aircraft maintenance.

Rod Selection

Welding rods are manufactured generally in 36-inch lengths. Steel rods in diameters from 1/32-inch to 1/4-inch, and cast iron rods from 3/16-inch to 1/2-inch are available.

The size of welding rod used is governed by the thickness of the metals being joined. If the rod is too small, it will not conduct heat away from the puddle rapidly enough and a burned weld will result. A rod that

Table 3. — Welding Rod Sizes For Sheet Thicknesses

Thickness of sheet (inches)	Diameter of rod (inches)
Under 0.115	1/16
0.115 to 0.220	3/32
0.200 to 0.315	1/8
0.315 to 0.500	5/32

is too large will chill the puddle. Since there are other factors that affect the desirable size of rod, the choices shown in Table 3 are suggestive only. As in selecting the proper size welding torch tip, experience will enable you to select the proper diameter welding rod.

It is poor economy to use anything other than high quality rod, as the risk of failure from inferior rods is not warranted by the slight difference in price. A respectable manufacturer's recommendation for a suitable rod may be accepted since the firm has usually made allowances in rod composition to compensate for any probable changes in filler and base metal caused by the welding process.

Safety In Welding

The importance of observing safety precautions when welding cannot be too highly stressed. Even though manufacturers have provided every possible safeguard in welding equipment, there still exists the possibility of injury when working with such substances as oxygen and acetylene. The characteristics of each one under pressure, and the high temperature produced by their union, make the observance of safety practices imperative.

Clothing

The welder's clothing should not provide places where flying sparks or pieces of molten metal can lodge to cause serious burns before they can be removed. Guard against open pockets, turned-up cuffs, or ragged holes in the clothing. Low shoes are also dangerous.

In aircraft welding, gloves are not often used because they make the handling of the light torch and rod rather cumbersome. Gloves are desirable for welding heavy metal or using the cutting torch. Gloves should be kept free from oil or grease, as such substances are likely to burst into flame upon contact with oxygen under pressure.

Opening Cylinder Valves

Before connecting a regulator to a new cylinder, the valve should be opened just enough to blow out any dirt in the valve outlet and then closed immediately to prevent excessive escape of gas. This opening to blow out dirt is known as CRACKING a valve. Stand to one side of the cylinder when you perform this operation.

Neither oxygen nor acetylene should be used directly from the cylinder. The proper regulator should be connected to reduce the pressure to a safe working volume. When the regulator is attached to the oxygen cylinder, the oxygen cylinder valve is opened very slowly at first to prevent damage to the regulator or gage. Oxygen valves should be opened by hand pressure only — never by a hammer or wrench. The oxygen cylinder should be opened fully after the pressure gage shows full pressure. The cylinder valve should never be opened until the regulator has been checked to make certain that the pressure regulating screw has been released.

When using the acetylene cylinder, the cylinder valve should be opened slowly about one-half turn and never more than one turn. This is done so that the gas can be cut off quickly in an emergency. For the same reason, the wrench is always left on the valve while the cylinder is in use.

Flashback And Backfire

Flashback and backfire are terms which are interpreted by many as being synonymous. The fact is that they differ greatly in quite a few respects.

A FLASHBACK occurs when the flame disappears from the end of the tip and the gases burn within the torch. This necessitates shutting off one or both of the gases to stop combustion within the torch. Flashbacks are often caused by loose connections, overheating of the torch, and improper pressures at the regulators.

A BACKFIRE is defined as a momentary return of the gases, not necessitating shutting off the gases as does a flashback. It is indicated in the torch by a snap or pop, the flame immediately recovering itself and burning at the tip in the usual manner. A backfire is rarely dangerous; however, the molten metal may be splattered when the flame pops. Chief causes for a backfire are: touching the tip against the work, overheating the tip, operating the torch at other than recommended gas pressures, a loose tip or head, or dirt in the seat.

Handling Cylinders

Both oxygen and acetylene cylinders must be handled with great care since they are charged with gases under high pressure. Neither should have the valves opened, other than for cracking, until the proper regulators have been attached.

When a cylinder must be moved a short distance, it should be rolled on its bottom while the protector cap is used as a pivot by one hand. When moved greater distances, cylinders should be handled with suitable trucks. Empty cylinders should never be used as rollers or supports. Valves should be kept closed. They should be marked EMPTY and returned to the supplier when the gases are exhausted.

Using Oxygen

The welder should keep in mind the fact that the characteristics that make oxygen useful are the same factors that make it dangerous. The ability to support combustion is useful when properly controlled, but dangerous if leaking oxygen ignites oil or grease on a cylinder, or anywhere on the welding equipment. OIL OR GREASE IS NEVER APPLIED TO ANY PART OF THE OXYGEN EQUIPMENT.

Oxygen helps to produce a useful flame for welding only when properly mixed with acetylene in the torch. No opportunity should be provided for it to mix with acetylene anywhere except in the torch. Oxygen cylinders should be stored separately from acetylene cylinders.

Oxygen should always be used for the purpose for which it is intended — never as a substitute for compressed air.

Using Acetylene

The proper use of acetylene requires an understanding of its explosive nature. Various mixtures of air and acetylene have been known to explode if ignited.

Acetylene cylinders are used only in an approximately upright position whenever possible to keep acetone from flowing into the lines. Acetylene is never used from a cylinder without first attaching a pressure reducing regulator to the cylinder. Acetylene should never be used from the cylinder faster than one-seventh of its capacity per hour, and free acetylene should not be used at pressures exceeding 15 p.s.i.

Goggles

At all times while welding, cutting, or observing welding work, the eyes should be protected by goggles designed for use with the oxyacetylene process. The light from the inner cone of the oxyacetylene flame is itself quite intense, but the hot metal in the section being welded produces a far greater glare. In addition, the eyes are so close to the work that it is advisable to protect them against flying sparks or bits of molten metal that may be splattered about. Goggles also protect the eyes from reflected heat which dries the surface of the eye, causing irritation.

Correct goggle lenses are made of special colored optical glass that minimizes the effect of glare and at the same time permits the operator to see his work clearly. Lenses are available in light, medium, or dark shades.

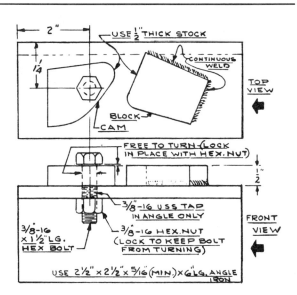

Tube Bending Simplified

This is an indispensable tool for forming tubing, formers, wing-tip bows, etc. Square tubing and flat stock can just as easily be formed.

Any old piece of angle iron (at least 5/16 in. or 3/8 in. thick) should be used. It can be clamped in a vise. (I should say, it should be so the forming or bending can be done very simple.)

The pivoting block is drilled slightly larger than the 3/8 in. bolt that goes through it, which in turn is screwed into the tapped hole in the top face of the angle iron. If a bend is made beyond the original curvature it can readily be brought back by just turning it in the jig and applying pressure.

The pivoting block automatically adjusts itself to the size material being used.

I made mine up so it would handle up to 1/2 in. stock and in less than 15 minutes formed a set of wing-tip bows for the Stits Playboy.

The material is inserted between the two blocks and bending is commenced where desired and slowly advanced while at the same time you're bending. Do this until the desired shape is formed. The pivoting block could also be made as a round plate and the hole drilled offset, but as I have drawn it, it works terrific.

by Iggy Polizzotto

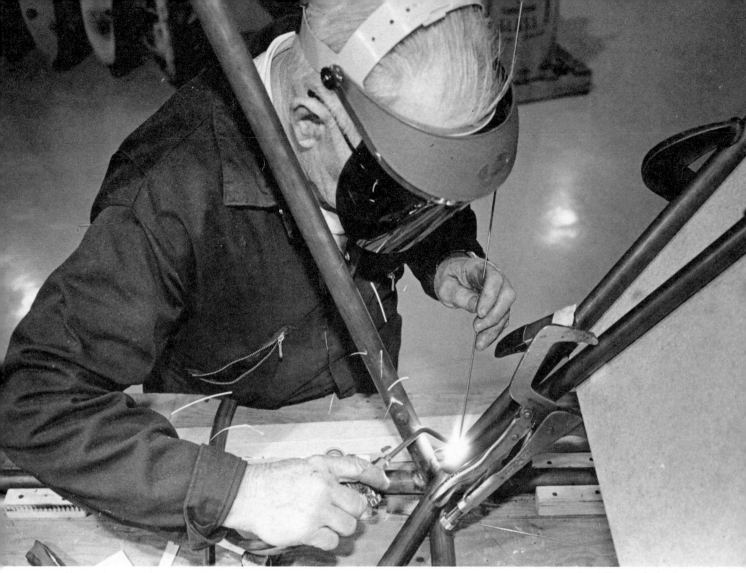

Proper holding of torch and feeding of welding rod are important. With practice, builders soon develop the skills needed to become expert welders.

Fundamental Welding Techniques

Holding The Torch

The first technique to master is the proper method of holding the welding torch. Two methods are recommended.

When welding light-gage (thin) metal, the hose should be draped over the outside of your wrist, and the torch held as though you were writing with it. For heavier work, a more comfortable grip is that in which the torch is held as you would hold a hammer, with the fingers curled underneath. To prevent fatigue allow the torch to balance in the hand.

Welding Positions

Whenever possible, it is desirable to make welds with the stock in a flat position. Figure 1. This facilitates puddle control, and the welder can work longer periods without tiring. These factors are so important that factories often use large jigs, or fixtures, to which the work is clamped, and which can be easily and quickly rotated by hand or by power to any desired angle.

Aircraft building and repair, however, involves the welding of so many different types of structures that it will quite often be necessary to do the welding in

OVERHEAD, VERTICAL, or HORIZONTAL positions, as well as in the normal FLAT position. Regardless of the position in which it is made, the weld must meet the same standards as to bead uniformity, reinforcement, and penetration.

Where the material is accessible from above, welds are made in the flat position, with the rod deposited from above. A horizontal weld is one in which the line of weld is horizontal but the surface of the work is vertical. In a vertical weld, both the line of weld and the surface of the work are vertical. An overhead weld is one in which the filler metal is deposited from the underside of the joint and the face of the joint is approximately horizontal.

Control Of Puddle

Welding in positions other than the flat is complicated chiefly by the fact that the molten puddle, affected by the pull of gravity, tends to seek a lower level. Fortunately, there are a number of forces tending to counteract the pull of gravity. These forces, operating in varying degrees in different positions, are: (1) cohesion of the puddle, (2) support provided by the weld metal (which has cooled) and by the base metal, (3) pressure of the flame against the end of the puddle, and (4) manipulation of the welding rod in the molten metal. Cohesion of the metal is directly affected by the heat of the welding flame. Too great an amount of heat makes the puddle more fluid, and therefore more likely to run.

Horizontal Welding

Practice in welding plate in different positions will develop the skill necessary to make welds in tubing since the welding of a single joint in tubing will often involve welding in several positions.

Welding in a horizontal position involves the carry-

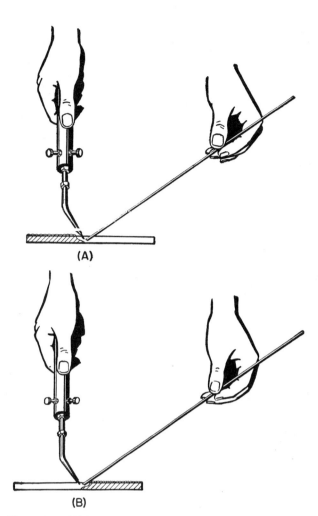

Figure 2. — (A) Forehand welding and (B) backhand welding.

ing of the bead from right to left (for the right-handed welder). In making a practice weld on plate, the pieces should be tacked while in the flat position, then either clamped in a jig or tacked to scrap stock so that the surfaces to be welded are held vertical. Adding the rod to the top of the puddle will help prevent the molten puddle from sagging to the lower edge of the bead. If the puddle is to have the greatest possible degree of cohesion, the puddle should not be allowed to become too hot.

Vertical Welding

Welding a vertical seam (which may be from 45 to 90 degrees to the horizontal) is not a great deal more difficult than horizontal welding. Vertical seams are ordinarily welded from the bottom up. Cohesion of the metal is not as effective a factor in combatting the pull of gravity in a vertical weld as in an overhead weld.

In a vertical weld, the pressure exerted by the torch flame must be relied upon, to a great extent, to support the puddle. It is highly important to keep the puddle from becoming hot enough to run. It may be necessary to remove the flame for an instant from the puddle to prevent overheating.

Vertical welds on plate are usually begun at the

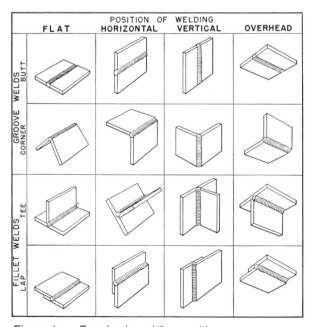

Figure 1. — Four basic welding positions.

	POSITION OF WELDING			
	FLAT	HORIZONTAL	VERTICAL	OVERHEAD
GROOVE WELDS / BUTT				
GROOVE WELDS / CORNER				
FILLET WELDS / TEE				
FILLET WELDS / LAP				

17

bottom, the puddle being carried up with a forehand motion. The tip should be inclined from 45 to 60 degrees, the exact angle depending upon the desired balance between correct penetration and control of the puddle. The rod is added from the top and in front of the flame.

Overhead Welding

In welding overhead, the puddle can be kept from sagging if it is not permitted to form in large drops. The rod is used to control the molten puddle. By constant movement of the rod, the molten metal is placed near the rear of the puddle. Less heat is required in an overhead weld because the heat naturally tends to rise.

Torch Motions

Two common methods of welding with the oxyacetylene torch are known as forehand and backhand.

The FOREHAND METHOD, used in welding most of the lighter gages of sheetmetal, is that in which the torch is pointed in the direction of travel, away from the completed bead, with the rod added in front of the flame. In this method of welding, the bead is carried from right to left for the right-handed welder.

The technique of BACKHAND WELDING is the reverse of forehand welding in most respects. As figure 2 indicates, the torch travel is from left to right (for the right-hand welder), with the flame being directed onto the completed weld. The rod follows the torch and is added between the flame and the finish weld.

An aircraft welder should be equally familiar with both welding methods in order to be able to perform the varied repairs required in aircraft work. Backhand welding is rarely used for sheetmetal welding because the increased amount of heat obtained by this method is likely to cause serious overheating in the lighter gages. However, in the quarter welding of tubing, the backhand method may be of value because of the superior control of the puddle which is possible with this method. This same improved control of the puddle makes it desirable to use backhand welding for heavy stock. Better fusion can be obtained in this heavier metal because it is possible to examine the progress of the weld, and to see that penetration is complete. For these heavier metals, backhand welding is also more economical since less heat is required. Added economy is due to the fact that the more rapid melting of the base metal makes greater welding speeds possible.

Torch And Rod Technique

The torch is held so that the flame points back toward the completed weld, care being taken to break down the edges and side walls of the base metal, and to fuse them to the required depth. The end of the filler rod is held in the molten puddle between the torch flame and the finished weld.

The rod is given a slight alternating movement toward and away from the flame when adding metal to the weld. This rod movement must be controlled so that the melting metal from the pool will not be pushed over on base metal which is not in a proper state of fusion to receive it.

When performing a weld, bring the torch down until the flame inner cone is about ⅛-inch away from the surface of the base metal. Hold it there until the flame melts a small puddle of metal, then insert the tip of the rod in this puddle. As the rod melts, gradually work the molten pool forward.

Do not move the torch ahead of the puddle, but work along the edges of the seam slowly enough to give the heat a chance to break down the edges. If the flame is moved ahead too rapidly, the heat will not penetrate deeply enough and the metal will not melt properly. On the other hand, don't be too slow about moving the flame along. If the flame is held in one place too long, the puddle will become too large and it may burn a hole through the metal.

Continue dipping the filler rod in the pool as the torch is advanced. Do not hold the rod so high that the molten metal from the end of the rod will fall drop by drop into the pool. This "raindrop" technique results in a finished weld full of pinholes.

Usually, it is not necessary to put the rod directly under the flame — the heat of the molten puddle will melt it. Keep th flame concentrated on the base metal.

There are four fundamental types of non-pressure welds — BEAD WELDS, FILLET WELDS, GROOVE WELDS, and PLUG WELDS. These types of welds are not necessarily intended to be exactly as shown in figure 3; they are merely representative of good practice.

Five fundamental types of welding joints are BUTT JOINT, T-JOINT, LAP JOINT, CORNER JOINT, and EDGE JOINT. These are illustrated in figure 4. Most of the welds can be used in various combinations to weld most of the joints, and it is readily seen that many hundreds of different types of welded joints can result from the combinations of these welds and joints.

Lap Joint

One of the basic types of welds is the lap joint on sheets, plates, or tubes. The lap weld in sheet or plate is commonly used in spot welding of stainless steel or

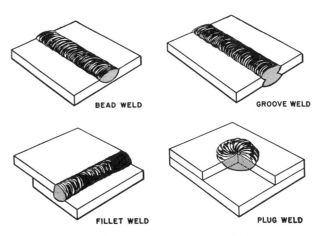

Figure 3. — Four fundamental types of welds.

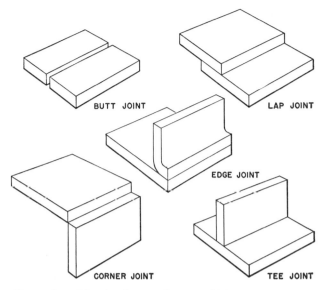

Figure 4. — Five fundamental types of joints.

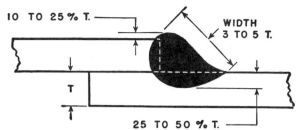

Figure 6. — Lap weld.

aluminium as a means of aircraft construction or repair. It is rarely used in oxyacetylene welding of flat stock because of its limitations of strength.

The single lap joint, shown in figure 5, has very little resistance to bending, and will not withstand the shearing stress to which the weld is subjected under tension or compression loads. It is therefore used for sheet, plate, and structural shapes where the load is not severe.

The double lap joint, illustrated in figure 5, has better strength characteristics than the single lap, but it requires nearly twice as much welding as the simpler and more satisfactory butt weld. It is used for sheet and plate parts where the welded sections must have greater strength.

An additional drawback to the use of a lap weld in aircraft welding is the added weight. A single lap weld is never used in welding of aluminum because of the difficulty of removing the flux from the joint.

Practice in welding lap joints in sheet or plate is desirable, because it helps you to develop the correct technique for fusing the edge of one part to the surface of another part without building the weld too high or burning away the top edge. This skill will be of value in the welding of structural tubing, or of collector rings and manifolds. The lap joint in tubing is superior to the butt weld, and is used for scarf and fishmouth splices, reduction splices, finger reinforcements or wrappers, and for silver soldering of fuel lines.

Lap Weld Practice Procedure

Overlap the sheets an amount sufficient to prevent the annealed zones outside the weld from overlapping. Do not have the metal directly on fire bricks as they

Figure 5. — Types of lap joints.

will absorb some of the heat from the welding flame.

Tack the plates at ¼- to ½-inch intervals (for steel one-sixteenth to one-eighth inch in thickness). After the tacks are made, the pieces should be hammered close together. If contact between the two plates is not maintained, there will be more of a tendency to burn away the exposed edge.

Weld from right to left if you are a right-handed welder. Direct the cone of the flame slightly more to the bottom plate, assuming the weld is made in a flat position. Add the rod at the top so as to keep the top edge from being cut back and to permit the heat to penetrate to the bottom of the weld. The formation of the correctly shaped bead is an indication that the heat is being properly directed, as figure 6 will explain.

A good lap weld has a fusion zone which includes 100 percent of the edge of the upper plate (in the flat position), and penetrates to a depth of 25 to 50 percent of the lower plate.

T-Joints

Where the end or edge of one piece is to be welded to the surface of another, the joint is called a **T**-joint. Such joints are quite common in aircraft construction, especially in tubular structures. Tee joints may also be

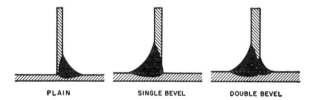

Figure 7. — Types of T-joints.

formed by welding one plate at approximately a right angle to another plate, or by welding tube to plate. These **T**-joints are illustrated in figure 7.

T-joints in tubing involve special technique in the actual welding, and will be considered in our discussion of aircraft tubing. The welding of a **T**-joint in plate is a rather simple process if the correct procedure is followed and the necessary precautions observed.

The plain **T**-joint in plate, which is welded from one side, requires no preparation other than cleaning the end of the vertical member and the surface of the horizontal member. This joint is suitable for most metal thicknesses used in aircraft work. Heavier thicknesses of stock will have the vertical member single or double beveled like the butt joint in order to permit thorough penetration.

T-Joint Practice Procedure

Put the two pieces of plate in position and tack them near the ends and at other points as required by the specifications for the metal (usually 1½ to 2 inches). The space between the horizontal and vertical members should not be greater than one thirty-second inch.

Begin welding at one end and proceed toward the opposite end slowly enough to get both pieces in a molten state at the same time. The tip should be directed toward the root of the weld at approximately a 45° angle, and tilted slightly forward. The rod should be added nearer the vertical member — that is, the rod should be added near the top of the fillet to prevent undercutting. Adding the rod here also permits the full flow of heat into the joint. The inner cone of the flame should be about one-eighth inch away from the surface.

Finish the weld, being careful not to apply too much heat to the vertical plate. If a tendency to undercut the vertical plate persists, play the flame more directly on the piece being undercut.

Precautions

Some results of faulty technique in welding a **T**-joint are UNDERCUTTING, POOR PENETRATION, INSUFFICIENT REINFORCEMENT, or TOO MUCH REINFORCEMENT. The undercutting can be avoided by applying the heat equally to both members, and by changing the torch angle as suggested in the preceding paragraph. Sufficient weld metal should be added to obtain a reinforcement in the throat of the fillet weld of 1¼ to 1½ times the thickness of the plate. Twenty-five percent of the vertical member at the throat of the weld should be a part of the fused zone; the fused zone should penetrate to 50 percent of the thickness of the horizontal plate. Extreme care must be observed at the start and finish of the weld to avoid overheating of the metal.

Corner Joints

Figure 8 illustrates the different types of corner joints commonly used in making tanks, boxes, and other articles from sheet and plate metals.

The closed type corner joint, shown in (A) of figure 8, is used on thin sheet metals where load stress is

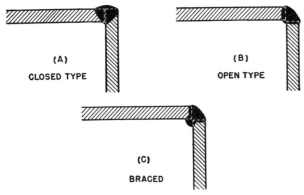

Figure 8. — Types of corner joints.

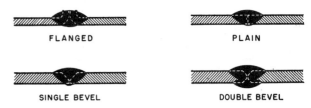

Figure 9. — Types of butt joints.

secondary. It is made by lapping one piece of stock over the other to fashion a corner. Because the edge of the overlapping sheet is melted down and fused to make the weld, little or no filler rod is added to the closed corner joint.

The open joint, as seen in (B) of figure 8, is used on heavier sheetmetal. The two edges are fused together and sufficient filler rod is added to form a well-rounded bead of weld metal on the outside. If such an open joint must bear a fairly heavy load, a weld is also made on the inside corner to give it greater strength, as demonstrated in (C).

Butt Joints

Figure 9 shows four methods of preparing a butt joint — that is, a joint in which the parts are joined end to end without overlapping. The FLANGED BUTT JOINT, in figure 9 is used for very thin sheetmetal up to 1/16-inch in thickness. The edges are prepared for welding by simply turning up a flange. The upstanding portion of the flange should extend above the upper surface of the sheet a distance equal to the thickness of the sheet. Flange welds are usually made without adding welding rod.

The PLAIN BUTT JOINT can be used for metals from 1/16- to 1/8-inch in thickness. A filler rod is used in making this joint in order to obtain a strong weld.

For metals thicker than 1/8-inch, it is necessary to bevel the edges so that the heat from the torch can penetrate completely through the base metal. A filler rod is also used for these welds.

Edge Joints

EDGE WELDS, as presented in figure 10, are excellent for fittings made up of two or more pieces of sheetmetal where the edges must be fastened together, and where load stresses are not important.

If the sheetmetal is thin, use the plain type in figure 10. That shown in (B) is better for heavier sections. Type (A) requires no filler rod, since on the thin material

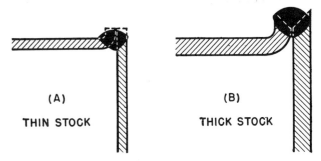

Figure 10. — Types of edge joints.

sufficient metal can be melted down to fill the seam while furnishing adequate reinforcement.

However, (B) of figure 10 is another story. Here the parts are thicker, and the edges must be beveled or grooved, and filler metal from a welding rod added in order to obtain a strong joint.

Any weld which joins two parts that are at right angles to each other is known as a FILLET WELD — thus edge joints, lap joints, and corner joints all require fillet welds.

Parts Of A Weld

Having learned the types of joints used in welding, our next step is to put this information to use. Let us first consider the parts of a weld, each of which has a name, as may be seen in figure 11.

Parts of a weld are the different areas of the weld metal and the base metal as related to each other in a welded joint. The term "weld metal" refers to the metal

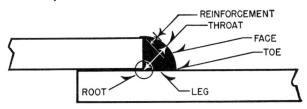

Figure 11. — Parts of a weld.

in a solidified weld. Base metal denotes the "parent" metal, or the metal in the parts joined as opposed to the metal added to secure the joint in welding. The terms for these areas may be classified as follows:

The FACE is the top or outer surface of a weld.

The ROOT of a weld is that part at the base of the joint.

The REINFORCEMENT is the amount of weld metal added above the surface of the base metal.

The THROAT OF A WELD is the distance from the root to the face, including the reinforcement.

The TOE OF A WELD is the edge or junction where the face of the weld and the base metal meet.

The LEG OF A WELD (fillet weld only) is one of the fusion surfaces, being the distance from the point where the original surfaces of the parts being welded intersect, to the toe of the weld. A fillet weld has two legs, as the lower drawing in figure 11 illustrates.

Appearance Of Weld

One of the best standards by which to judge the quality of a weld, and the one most commonly used in aircraft work, is the APPEARANCE OF THE WELD. The smoothness and regularity of the bead, the presence of fused-in edges along the seam, the amount of reinforcement, and the appearance of the weld opposite the bead are fairly reliable indications of the soundness of a weld.

A properly designed welded joint is stronger than the base metal which it joins. The characteristics of a welded joint that has been properly made are discussed in the following paragraphs.

Reinforcement And Bead

Reinforcement of a weld, as we have seen, is the amount of filler material that is built up above the surface of the base metal. The metal that is deposited during the welding process is referred to as the bead.

It is obvious that reinforcement and bead are so closely related that specifications for one directly affect the other. The reinforcement added varies according to the type of weld — butt, lap, or fillet — and according to the thickness of the metal. Sufficient rod must be added to a butt joint to build up the reinforcement 25 to 50 percent of the thickness of the base metal, or the tensile strength of the joint will be inadequate for the loads applied. The bead should be wide enough to tie in or fuse the weld metal with the base metal on each side of the joint. The bead should merge smoothly with the surface, as shown in figure 12, without undercutting or excessive build-up.

Adding too much rod to the puddle is likely to cause the filler metal to roll over onto the solid metal past the fusion line of the puddle. The recommended specifications for butt, lap, and fillet welds are shown in connection with the requirements for penetration in these welds.

Penetration

Penetration is the depth of fusion in a weld. Thorough fusion is the most important characteristic which contributes to a sound weld. In the lighter gages of metal, the normal depth of puddle will insure proper penetration. A normal depth of puddle will be secured if the following precautions are observed: (1) leave a small space (one-half the thickness of the metal) between the edges to be joined, (2) use correct heat, and (3) manipulate the torch and rod properly.

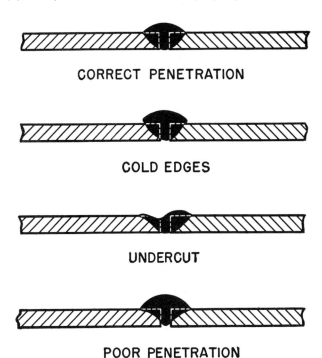

Figure 12. — Penetration of welds.

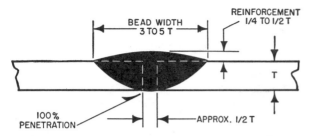

Figure 13. — Butt weld, showing width and depth of bead.

Correct torch manipulation involves holding the torch at the angle best suited to the type of joint and to the position in which the job is being welded. It requires moving the torch along the seam rapidly enough to prevent burning holes in the metal, and yet slowly enough to permit fusion to the bottom of the joint.

Penetration is also affected by the size of the rod, and where and how it is added. Too small a rod will not conduct the heat away from the puddle, and a burned weld will result. Too large a rod chills the puddle before complete fusion has been secured. Some jobs require manipulation of the rod to keep the consistency of the puddle constant, and to keep it from falling.

Corrosion or rust, particularly in lower steel tube structures of older airplanes parked outside or in storage over lengthy periods of time is always a problem. Here welder has fitted a section of new tubing in the control surface of 1927 antique aircraft undergoing restoration.

Spacing And Penetration

Heavier gages of metal — over one-eighth inch — require preparation before actual welding begins to secure penetration of the weld metal to the desired depth. As previously stated, a space between plates equal to one-half the thickness of the base metal is sufficient for sheetmetal. Metals more than one-eighth inch and less than one-half inch in thickness must be single beveled to an included angle of 90°. When the metal is more than one-half inch in thickness, it should be double beveled.

To maintain the spacing decided upon, it is necessary to tack weld the plates. The number of tacks to be used will be determined by the thickness and composition of the metal.

Specifications For Bead And Penetration

In a butt weld, the penetration should be 100 percent of the thickness of the base metal. When penetration is complete in this type of weld, the edges opposite the bead have completely disappeared by fusion, yet no drops of fused metal are evident. The width and depth of bead are shown in figure 13.

On a fillet weld, the penetration requirements are 25 to 50 percent of the thickness of the base metal, as

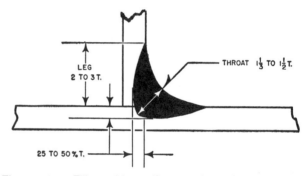

Figure 14. — Fillet weld specifications for bead and penetration.

may be seen in figure 14. To determine whether it has been obtained, examine a cross-section of the weld that has been filed and polished. In this weld, the presence of oxide scale on the side opposite the root of the weld is an indication of the depth of fusion.

Checking Expansion And Contraction

There are a number of useful methods used in keeping expansion and contraction of metal under control. These methods include tacking the material; employing clamps, jigs, or chill bars; rapid welding; backstep welding; stagger (skip) welding; and, in some cases, preheating the entire piece.

Preheating the entire section of the metal before beginning the welding operation aids in bringing about a uniform contraction when the weld is finished.

Either stagger or backstep welding may be used in rapid welding. Either of these techniques distributes the heat evenly over the length of the seam, resulting in uniform expansion and contraction.

Sometimes a second torch is needed as with this repair job. Torch at left is used to preheat tubing prior to making repair weld on antique aircraft.

Techniques For Ferrous Metals

Precautions

The term, FERROUS, applies to the group of metals having iron as the principal constituent. Repair by welding of aircraft parts composed of ferrous metals is done only under the following conditions:

1. When the piece to be welded is made of non-heat-treated metal, or, if heat-treated, when facilities are available to reheat-treat.
2. When the metal has not been cold-worked.
3. When the piece has not been brazed or soldered at its joints.

A welder should not repair heat-treated aircraft parts by welding unless facilities are available for re-heat-treating. Also, steel parts that depend upon cold-working for their strength are not welded because the heat of the welding flame destroys such strength. Nor should parts made of cold-rolled steel — which include streamline wires, cables, tie rods, and solid drawn wire — be welded.

Steel parts with brazed or soldered joints are never welded by the oxyacetylene method because the brazing or soldering mixture penetrates the hot steel and spoils the weld.

Since heat treatment and cold working are both employed to give metals greater strength, airplane designers make extensive use of heat-treated and cold-worked metal, especially in structural members. Therefore, a welder is correct in deducing from this fact that there are many repair jobs on structural airplane parts that are "out-of-bounds" for his particular skills.

Preparation For Welding

Proper preparation for welding is an important factor in every welding operation.

The edges of the parts to be joined must be prepared in accordance with the joint design chosen. The edges must be CLEAN. Arrangements must be made for holding the parts in proper alinement and for preheating, if this is required.

The first step in preparing an aircraft part for welding is to strip it of all dirt, grease or oil, and any protective coating such as cadmium plating, enamel, paint, or varnish. Such coating not only hampers welding, but also mingles with the weld to prevent good fusion.

Cadmium plating can be chemically removed by dipping the edge to be welded in one of the following solutions:

1. A mixture of 73 cubic centimeters of hydrochloric acid, 27 cubic centimeters of water, and 2 grams of antimony trioxide.
2. A mixture of 1 pound of ammonia nitrate and 1 gallon of water.
3. A mixture of 3 gallons of water, 7½ gallons of hydrochloric acid, and 1½ pints of ammonia nitrate.

Enamel, paint, or varnish may be removed by buffing with a wire brush, by the application of emery cloth, by sandblasting, by the use of a paint or varnish solvent, or by treating the piece with a 10 percent caustic soda solution followed with a thorough washing with hot water to remove the solvent and residue.

Sandblasting is the most efficient method of removing rust or scale from steel parts. If dirt, grease, or oil is present, use a one-to-one carbon tetrachloride-naptha solution or a caustic acid solution.

Carbon Steel

The iron-carbon alloys may be classified as steel if they contain from 0.01 to 1.7 percent carbon, and cast iron if they contain from 1.7 to 4 percent carbon.

Practically all weldable steels in aircraft construction contain less than 0.44 percent carbon. There are a few exceptions, such as the high-carbon fine steel wires which are resistance welded and then braided into cables.

The techniques used in welding low- and medium-carbon steel are more or less basic, although these materials are usually handled in general shop work and not on aircraft. Welding high-carbon steel and alloy steel — for example, stainless steel — requires a similar technique with the addition of certain special precautions.

In general, low- and medium-carbon steels require no preheating. The parts must be thoroughly cleaned, however, and each edge of joints on thick pieces must be beveled down to a 45° angle. A flux is not required. For these steels, a filler rod of low-carbon steel, containing a small percentage of vanadium, is used. The torch flame must be adjusted to neutral, carefully avoiding an oxidizing flame which burns or oxidizes the metal.

General Procedure

In welding carbon steel, use the forehand method, holding the torch at a 60° angle to the surface of the work. The tip of the inner cone should not quite touch the molten metal.

If the piece of steel is comparatively thick — that is, plate steel rather than sheet steel — use a swinging motion with the torch to make certain that the metal on each side of the groove melts thoroughly. As the torch is swung from side to side of the groove, the edges begin to break down and metal flows in the bottom of the groove.

While this process of breaking down the edges is

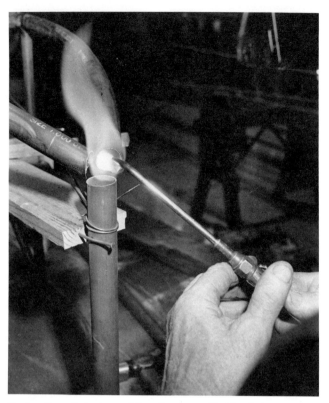

Preheating of cluster welds or heavy wall tubing is important so that when welding proper fusion of all elements takes place.

taking place, the filler rod should be held in the outer cone of the torch flame to heat it. By the time the pool of molten steel has been formed at the bottom of the groove, the filler rod should be almost at the melting point.

As the weld proceeds, filler metal from the rod should be added until the surface of the weld is built up slightly above the edge of the parts. This additional metal provides reinforcement.

The preceding explanation refers to thick pieces of low- or medium-carbon steel. But whether welding thin or thick pieces of steel, it is necessary to critically observe the molten puddle. When it has been built sufficiently high above the surface of the steel, gradually advance the puddle of molten metal along the seam. Be extremely careful, however, not to extend the pool of molten metal until the sides of the groove have been broken down by heat. The reason for this is elementary. Molten filler metal deposited on base metal that is hot but still in a solid state does not fuse. Instead of fusion, the result is adhesion, which is nothing more than soft soldering.

Good fusion is not difficult to obtain, although iron oxide, or scale, in steel melts slightly before the metal does and may be mistaken for molten metal. Remember that a fusion weld is not produced until the metal itself actually melts.

As the end of the seam is approached, raise or tilt the torch flame slightly to chill the molten steel enough to prevent it from flowing over the edge and burning the metal.

The welding principles described above apply

equally to high-carbon steel, which owes most of its special physical and mechanical characteristics to its comparatively high-carbon content — at least 0.50 percent. A welding flame with too much oxygen or acetylene will directly affect the characteristics of this steel by changing its carbon content. A carburizing flame (excess acetylene) adds carbon to the weld and makes it hard and brittle. An oxidizing flame (excess oxygen) burns the weld.

High-carbon filler rods aid in maintaining the hardness of steel which is to be heat-treated for increased hardness and strength. Satisfactory results can be obtained with medium-carbon filler rod on thinner sections when considerable intermingling of base metal and filler metal occurs. With the medium-carbon rod, a weld of moderate strength and increased ductility is possible.

Stainless Steel

Steels popularly known as stainless steels are actually corrosion-resisting, although they are not fully resistant to all corrosive agents. Corrosion resistance of stainless steels is determined by the surface condition of the metal, composition of the metal, and temperature and concentration of the corrosive agent.

Corrosion-resistant steel is an alloy steel which includes among its alloying elements chromium or chromium and nickel, which are added to increase corrosion-resisting properties. Slight variations of the chemical composition of these steels produce marked changes in their qualities.

Types Of Stainless Steel

Due to their sensitivity to change in chemical composition, a great many types of corrosion resistant steels have been developed, although in general they fall into three classifications or groups:
1. Chromium-nickel steel.
2. Hardenable chromium steel.
3. Nonhardenable chromium steel.
The steels used by the aircraft industry are chiefly of the CHROMIUM-NICKEL group. This group includes those steels containing 17 to 25 percent chromium, 7 to 13 percent nickel, and 0.20 percent or less of carbon. The well-known "18-8" steel (18 percent chromium, 8 percent nickel) is one of this group.

18-8 STEEL is the corrosion-resistant steel for which the aircraft industry finds the greatest use. It is divided into two groups dependent on their uses in aircraft construction — structural and nonstructural. The structural group has high strength, ease of fabrication, and corrosion resistance, while the nonstructural group is distinguished by its excellent corrosion resistance and heat-resisting qualities such as are required in exhaust collector systems.

The aircraft welder will be concerned only with the nonstructural group of 18-8 steels, for reasons which will be explained in the following paragraphs.

The 18-8 steels in the nonstructural group attain an ultimate tensile strength of 80,000 p. s. i. and an elongation of 40 percent. By comparison, the 18-8 steels in the structural group attain an ultimate tensile strength of 80,000 to 300,000 p. s. i. This great strength is obtained by cold working — such as drawing or rolling — and will be lost if heat is applied. This fact eliminates the possibility of using heat as a means of fabrication and limits its use almost exclusively to parts which can be spot welded.

Stainless steel of the 18-8 nonstructural type may be obtained in sheet form and as welded or seamless tubing. Welded tubing is less expensive than seamless tubing and is often used in the manufacture of exhaust collectors. Sheet and tubing with a wall thickness of 0.042- to 0.049-inch have proved satisfactory for this purpose.

This material is used primarily for nonstructural parts such as exhaust collectors, stacks, or manifolds. It is practically nonmagnetic in its annealed state and is sometimes used for special purposes, especially in the vicinity of compasses.

All operations necessary for the fabrication of exhaust collectors can be done cold with this steel. The material hardens as it is worked, but it seldom requires annealing before an operation by cold working is completed.

Sheet stock can be bent cold through an angle of 180° without cracking over a radius equal to the thickness of the sheet. Tubing can be bent to an inside radius of two diameters, although a larger radius is preferable.

Oxyacetylene Welding Of 18-8 Steel

The welding equipment used for the welding of ordinary steels can be used for welding nonstructural corrosion-resisting 18-8 steel. The procedure for welding this material is also basically the same as that for ordinary steels. The only difference lies in the fact that certain special precautions must be followed carefully in order to obtain the most desired results.

Preliminaries

Precautions to be taken in welding stainless steel begin with the welding flame. A slightly reducing flame is recommended for use with 18-8 steel. By adjusting the flame so that the feather around the inner cone is about one-sixteenth inch in length, the exact amount of excess acetylene will be obtained.

Protection is thus assured against any variations in gas pressure tending to change a strictly neutral flame into an oxidizing flame. Special care must be exercised to avoid a flame with too much oxygen, as such flame oxidizes the molten metal and renders it porous. Make certain, however, that the flame does not have so much excess acetylene that the stainless steel will be loaded up with carbon and lose its resistance to corrosion.

Use a torch tip one or two sizes smaller than those prescribed for similar gages of plain steel.

The flux should be one especially compounded to dissolve the chromium oxide which forms on the molten stainless steel. Mix the flux with water to form a thin paste. Flux also may be mixed with alcohol or shellac. Apply the flux to the underside of the seam to protect the hot metal from the air and consequent oxidation.

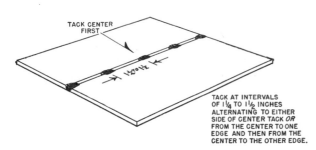

TACK CENTER FIRST

TACK AT INTERVALS OF 1¼ TO 1½ INCHES ALTERNATING TO EITHER SIDE OF CENTER TACK *OR* FROM THE CENTER TO ONE EDGE AND THEN FROM THE CENTER TO THE OTHER EDGE.

Figure 1. — Tacking methods.

Allow the flux to dry for several minutes after it is brushed on so that it becomes fairly solid before the weld is begun.

The filler rod should be of the same composition as the base metal. If the base metal is columbium-treated, then a columbium-treated stainless steel filler rod should be selected. A filler rod is always required when the pieces to be welded are one-sixteenth inch or thicker.

If the pieces are thin — that is, up to one-sixteenth inch in thickness — the common treatment is to turn up flanges on each edge to a height equal to the metal thickness. The flanges are painted on both top and bottom with flux, then melted down to form a smooth, moderately reinforced weld. In this instance a filler rod is not required, as the flanges furnish sufficient metal to fill the seam.

Tacking is one of the means of lessening warping and distortion by holding the stainless steel in alinement for the welding process. Thin sheets which are to be butt-welded should be tacked at intervals of 1¼ to 1½ inches. Tacking may be accomplished by either one of two methods, both of which require the first tack to be placed at the center of the joint. One method requires the placing of the tacks at correct intervals from the central tack toward one end and then tacking from the central tack toward the opposite end. The other method is effected by placing alternate tacks on each side of the central tack until the ends have been secured. These methods are illustrated in figure 1.

If the parts to be welded are between one-sixteenth and one-eighth inch in thickness, join the edges in a plain butt weld. A bucking strip of copper should be placed beneath the seam to prevent the molten metal from flowing out of the weld and to absorb some of the welding heat. If the parts are one-eighth inch or thicker, bevel the edges to provide a **V** in order to permit heat from the torch flame to penetrate completely through the metal.

Controlling Expansion Of 18-8 Steel

Stainless steel will conduct heat only about 40 percent as rapidly as mild steel, but its coefficient of expansion is about 50 percent greater. These properties cause warping or distortion, especially when the material being welded is thin, unless suitable precautions are taken.

This warping and distortion can be prevented or lessened to a great extent by the use of clamps, copper chill plates, and jigs, or a combination of these appliances to hold the metal in alinement while it is being welded and while the weld is cooling. A precaution to observe when using this method is that the metal must not be clamped too tightly because it tends to buckle and crack if it is not permitted to expand and contract slightly.

Place the parts to be welded so that the line of the weld slants slightly downward in the direction of the welding. This allows the flux, which melts at a lower temperature than the metal, to flow forward and provide protection for the metal as it fuses.

Welding Procedure

Either the forehand or backhand methods of welding are approved for operations on 18-8 steel, although the former is preferable for thin sheetmetal while the backhand method is recommended for heavier pieces.

When welding 18-8 steel, puddling of the weld should be prevented or minimized as much as possible because it increases the tendency toward oxidation and separation of valuable constituents.

In the actual welding operation, the flame should be directed forward in order to preheat the metal ahead of the area being welded. The torch is held at an angle of 80° to the surface of the work, with the tip of the flame's inner cone maintained about one-sixteenth inch from the work so that the flame is forced down into the weld. The rod, on the other hand, is held just above the weld and in the flame so that it melts and drops down into the weld as the work progresses.

A relatively small tip is used on the torch to permit slow, careful welding without danger of overheating. Excessive heat on molten columbium-treated 18-8 steel increases the loss of columbium during the welding and should be avoided.

Welds should be completed with thorough penetration in one pass (the layer of weld metal deposited in one trip of the torch and rod down the length of the seam) if at all possible. It is customary and advisable

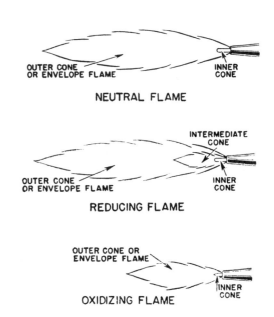

OUTER CONE OR ENVELOPE FLAME

INNER CONE

NEUTRAL FLAME

OUTER CONE OR ENVELOPE FLAME

INTERMEDIATE CONE

INNER CONE

REDUCING FLAME

OUTER CONE OR ENVELOPE FLAME

INNER CONE

OXIDIZING FLAME

to weld stainless steel entirely from one side. Care should be taken to completely fill the seam so that no point will have to be reworked.

It is important not to stop or to retrace a hot weld. If this is necessary, the weld should cool completely before being reworked. If it should be necessary to go back over a weld, or if there is need for welding at the back side of the seam in order to support points of severe stress, the entire seam should be preheated before the flame is applied to any local area of the joint. This type of preheating, while necessary, is undesirable because the metal is apt to warp and slow cooling is harmful to stainless steel.

Never start at the edge of a seam and work toward the center. If the joint is in such position that working in from an edge is absolutely necessary, the best policy is to begin the weld at a point an inch or two in from the edge. Weld in from this starting point until that section of the seam is finished, then return to the starting point and weld out toward the edge to complete the weld. This procedure will avoid excessive distortion.

Properties Of The Welded Area

The welder of stainless steel is concerned not only with the preservation of the strength of the material, but is also responsible for the maintenance of the corrosion resistant quality of the material across the weld zone. Steels of the 18-8 group are best able to resist corrosion when in their normal austenitic condition. This condition is obtained by heating to approximately 1,900° F., and then quickly cooling to the black (in 3 minutes or less).

In those stainless steels which do not contain columbium or titanium, prolonged exposure to heat in a range from 800° to 1,500° F. will cause the chromium in the steel to combine with the carbon to form carbides, which precipitate along the grain boundaries. These carbides are subject to attack by corrosive agents, such as salt spray or water. Those steels without columbium or titanium are therefore seriously weakened if heated to the range just mentioned and allowed to cool slowly.

Universal Welding Jig

Jigging tubing for tack welding can present problems. When not enough hands are available it becomes difficult to hold tubing in proper position during welding — or as the torch passes near. Two or three of the devices shown here, however, will solve the problem by holding the tubes stable and in the proper position for tack welding.

Making a slot — rather than holes in the bar stock — would increase the adjustability of the jig. A longer bar would also increase the reach of the jig.

by Harold Gallatin

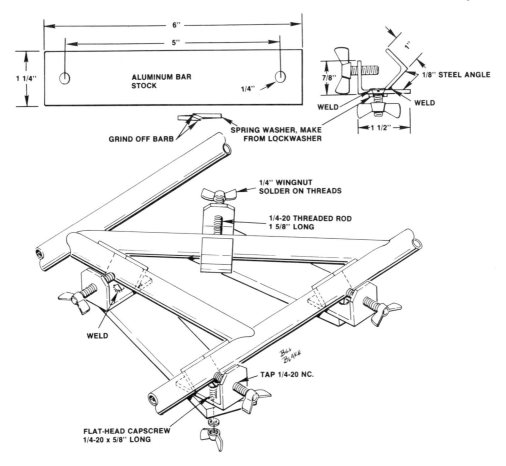

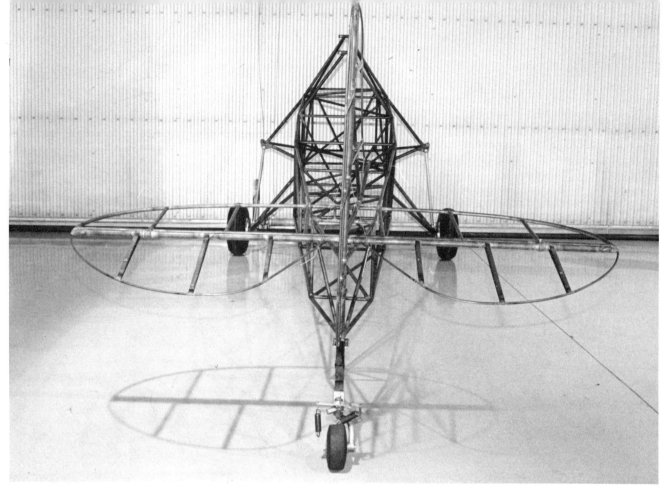

Corben Super Ace under construction with primary steel tube structures completed and assembled to check fit and accuracy.

Welding Aircraft Tubing

Tube Welding Techniques

When welding, the builder will be more concerned with tubing than with flat stock, since the fuselage, engine mounts, landing gears, and collector rings, are parts made of steel tubing. Because the shapes of the tube ends involved in welded joints and splices are not as simple as the parts of a joint in sheet or plate, preparation of tubing joints requires more time and more careful workmanship.

The welding of tubing involves the fundamental techniques used in the welding of flat stock, but several practices may be required on the same joint. For example, a butt joint in tubing might be welded partly by forehand and partly by backhand welding. This same joint, if welded in the fixed position, might require welding in the flat, vertical, and overhead positions.

In addition to adapting techniques to tubular shapes, the aircraft welder must have an understanding of the reaction of high-strength alloys under the welding flame if he is to successfully weld tubing made of these alloys.

Tubing Materials

At one time, fuselage and wing structures were made of mild carbon steel (S. A. E. 1025) almost exclusively. This steel has been replaced for most uses by CHROME MOLYBDENUM STEEL (S. A. E. X4130) because of the latter's superior tensile and fatigue strengths, its corrosion resistance, and its shock impact resistance. For these reasons the characteristics of this metal under the welding flame must be clearly understood.

STAINLESS STEEL of the 18-8 type is also widely used in the fabrication of collector rings and other exhaust system parts because of its great corrosion resistance and its high tensile strength and ductility.

Tubing Joints

Tubing joints are different from joints in flat stock — not only in shape, but in the amount of strength developed. For example, the plain butt joint in sheet or plate is seldom used in tubular construction. As shown in figure 1, welding such a joint develops annealed areas or zones parallel to the bead that are so weakened as to fail by buckling or wrinkling. Consequently, for butt joins a weld called the FISHMOUTH JOINT or a weld called the SCARF JOINT is used.

A FISHMOUTH JOINT is a tubular joint used in joining two pieces of tubing end to end, in which the edges are cut to resemble a fish's mouth. For pieces of equal diameter a BUTT JOINT with the joining edges of both pieces cut in matching fishmouths is used. For pieces of unequal diameter, a REDUCTION JOINT with only the end of the larger piece fishmouth-cut is used.

A SCARF JOINT is a joint between two members in line with each other, in which the joining ends of one or both pieces are cut diagonally at an angle of about 30° from a center line. This is called a scarf cut. In welding aircraft tubing, scarf joints are used both as butt joints and reduction joints.

The joint referred to above as a REDUCTION JOINT is that made between two members of unequal diameter or width, both members being of the same general plane — that is, not at an angle to each other. Reduction joints are used in the welding of aircraft tubing to join tubes end to end for greater length as in longeron construction; to repair defective sections of tubing, or to brace a section of a piece of tubing. When additional length is the main purpose, the end of the smaller tube is telescoped into the end of the larger tube, far enough for adequate bracing. A welded joint of this type is often called a TELESCOPE JOINT. When repair or bracing of a central section is the main purpose, a short section of larger tubing is slipped over the smaller tube like a sleeve.

Where greater strength than that obtainable with either the scarf or fishmouth butt joint is desired, SPLICES using sleeves are commonly used. These splices are particularly adaptable to the repair of tubular structures, such as engine mounts. Specifications for repairs using these splices will vary with individual aircraft. One rather common restriction is that no welds can be made in the middle third of a tube section, as that is the section most likely to be distorted by compression or bending stresses.

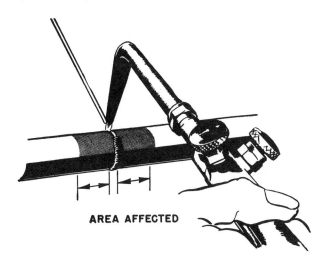

Figure 1. — Annealed areas set up in butt-welded joint.

Table 1. — Tip Sizes For Oxyacetylene Welding Of Chrome Molybdenum Tubing

Thickness of steel	Diameter of hole in tip	Drill size
0.015 to 0.031	0.026	No. 71
.031 to .065	.031	No. 68
.065 to .125	.037	No. 63

Chrome-Molybdenum Welding Techniques

Chrome-molybdenum is easy to weld, has a high initial strength, and is extremely shock-resistant. Code name for the most common kind of chome-moly is S. A. E. 4130.

The oxyacetylene flame is generally preferred for thin-walled tubing made of chrome molybdenum. For material 0.093 inch and thicker, the electric arc is preferred, as the heat zone is narrower, resulting in less distortion from expansion.

The welding technique with the oxyacetylene flame is the same as that required for the carbon steels, except that the area surrounding the weld should be heated to 300°-400° F. before starting the weld. This is necessary, as a sudden application of the flame without some preliminary heating sometimes causes cracks in the heated area.

The flame should be directed on the metal during welding at such an angle that preheating takes place ahead of the weld. A soft neutral flame must always be used, as an oxidizing flame burns and weakens the steel. A carburizing flame renders the metal brittle and may also cause cracks on cooling. The volume of flame should be just large enough to reduce the base metal to a melting state so that the proper fusion will take place. Overheating will set up severe stresses, and will cause excessive grain growth, which contributes to low strength in the welds and in the adjacent area of the base metal. The weld metal should be protected from the air as much as possible while hot.

Chrome molybdenum tubing is quite generally welded with a low carbon (mild steel) rod, welds of satisfactory strength and ductility resulting if the correct techniques are used.

A chrome molybdenum rod may be used for joints requiring high strength, if the part can be heat treated after welding. No flux is required. Better results will be obtained if the welds are not begun at the raw edge (as of a gusset), since the metal may crack. Nor should the torch be lifted suddenly from the metal at the end of a weld, as this may cause a pinhole, at which point stresses would be concentrated.

Table 1 indicates recommended tip sizes for oxyacetylene welding of chrome molybdenum tubing.

Welds in aircraft tubing must not be dressed (filed or smoothed down) unless further welding is to be performed on the dressed section. If the weld is on thin tubing — less than 0.040 inch — it should not be wider than one-quarter inch.

Precautions

Before beginning a weld, clean the parts thoroughly by taking off all grease, paint, or other foreign substances from the section to be repaired.

Remember also that chrome-molybdenum steel is strong and tough when cool, but it is weak at high temperatures. Because of this trait, the metal may crack if subjected to even a comparatively slight stress while in a white-hot condition. Therefore, the rule to follow with hot chrome-moly is — handle with care.

Such handling requires that the following two specific precautions be taken. (1) Never use welding jigs that will hamper expansion or contraction of welded members. These two familiar reactions — contraction and expansion — which occur to some degree in all metals when heat is applied, are present when welding chrome-molybdenum aircraft tubing. (2) Be extremely careful to avoid overheating and burning the metal when welding near or at an edge. Edges heat up quickly, and welds started at a raw edge may cause the metal to crack.

It is also important to prevent loss of metal thickness from excessive scaling (formation of iron oxide).

The torch should not be lifted suddenly from the metal at the end of a weld because of the danger of creating a pinhole. A good technique is to "fan" the end of the weld with flame when finishing the bead. This prevents sudden chilling of the puddle.

Cracking may be prevented by cutting down the strain caused either by the weight of the parts or by the restriction of normal expansion and contraction. For this reason, when welding chrome-molybdenum tube assemblies, good technique demands that one end of the web member be completely welded to the flange member of a truss, and the weld be allowed to cool before welding of the opposite end of the web member is begun.

Similarly, joints of an assembly in which several members terminate should be welded first and allowed to cool before attempting to weld the opposite ends. Assuming that these members are connected to similar joints at their opposite ends, heavy clamps, chill plates, or wet asbestos should be used on the members near the weld. This procedure aids in preventing expansion, caused by heat travel, to adjacent parts. As can be readily seen, welding a number of joints terminating in such an assembly naturally takes more time and requires more heat than merely welding a single member into a joint. Consequently, there is a great amount of expansion.

In welding fittings, shrinkage strains and the consequent danger of cracking can be checkmated by starting the weld at the fixed end of the seam and working toward the open end.

It is good practice to relieve the stresses of alloy steel parts after welding by a process known as drawing off. This means heating the entire part uniformly to a temperature between 1,150° and 1,200° F., then permitting it to cool slowly. If equipment is not available for heating the entire piece, the same effect can be obtained by using the torch to heat the part for a radius of several inches around the weld area.

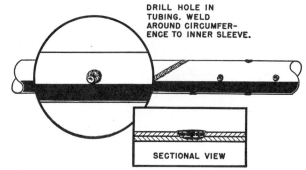

Figure 2. — Rosettes.

If a joint is to be secured both by riveting and welding, aline the rivet holes and complete all welding before the rivets are driven. If this procedure is reversed, expansion and contraction forces develop a shearing stress on the rivets and tend to stretch, or elongate, the rivet holes.

In welding tubing assemblies, warping can be controlled by the use of sufficient clamps and the proper kind of jigs.

Quarter welding, a variation of skip welding, is used to help prevent distortion. To quarter weld, tack-weld the tubing joint at four equidistant points, then weld diametrically opposite segments from tack to tack. Skip welding throughout the piece also aids in reducing distortion. A typical tubing repair in which quarter welding is recommended will be discussed later.

Major Repairs

Unless the damage to members of a steel tube structure is comparatively slight, the following procedure should be followed: remove the injured part and weld in either a partial replacement tube or an entirely new piece of tubing. The tubing used for telescope reinforcement or splicing must be of at least the same tensile strength and wall thickness as the original member.

Tubes and sections are always cut out with a hacksaw — never by oxyacetylene flame cutting. Tubes inserted as replacements are then joined at their ends by means of a splice.

Splicing of partial tube replacements may be done by using a replacement tube of the same diameter plus either internal or external reinforcing sleeves, or by using an external replacement tube of the next larger diameter. Such a replacement tube is spliced to the stub ends of the original tubing.

Each type of splice has its particular advantage and use, even though the methods involved in making them are essentially the same. If the original damaged tube included castings or fittings that have been made to fit the tube, then the spliced replacement tube must be of the same diameter as the original tubing. Therefore, either internal or external reinforcing sleeves under or over the splices can be used. If no fittings are attached to the original tubing, the replacement can usually be an external tube.

Rosettes are often added to a splice (see figure 2) to increase the shear strength of the repaired member.

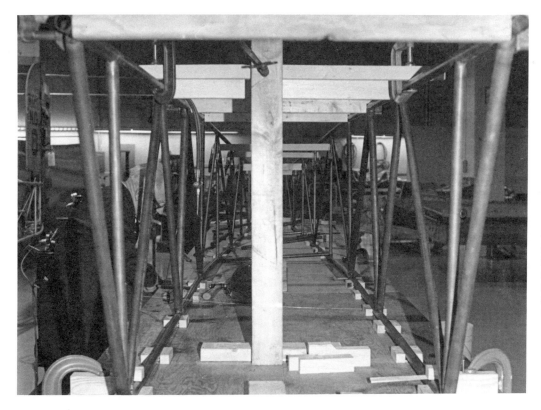

No problem with alignment when measurements are accurate and fuselage sides are rigidly clamped into position as shown here.

Holes are drilled in a staggered formation around the outer tube. These holes should be a diameter equal to one-fourth of the tube diameter, but not less than one-fourth inch. The rosette is welded around the inner edge of the hole into the smaller telescoped tube after all other welds on the joint have been completed.

Only one partial replacement tube can be inserted in any one section of a structural member. If more than one tube in a joint is damaged, remove the entire joint and insert a new, preassembled and welded joint of the proper design.

If a web member is damaged at a joint so that it is impossible to retain at that point a stub long enough to permit splicing on replacement tubing, put in an entirely new web member.

If a continuous longeron is damaged at a joint, make certain that the replacement tube splices on either side of the joint are far enough from the joint to prevent weakening the weld. First cut loose the web member at the affected joint and remove the damaged section of tubing. Then splice the replacement tubing to the stub ends of the original section of longerons. Finally, weld the web member to the new section of longeron tubing. Use wooden braces to hold the tubes in alinement during the repair.

Inner And Outer Sleeve Reinforcements

In figure 3 is shown a partial replacement tube spliced to the original tubing by means of inner reinforcing sleeves. In this procedure, a minimum of welding is required, and consequently there is less chance of weakening or distorting the tubing. This method has the advantage of giving a smooth outer surface to the repaired section.

In making this repair, first make diagonal cuts in the affected tubing, ascertaining that the cuts are located away from the middle third of the affected tube section. When the part has been removed, file off the burr, or roughness, from the edges of the cuts, select a replacement tube matching the damaged original tubing in both diameter and wall thickness, and cut from it a length one-fourth inch less than that of the removed section, by means of similar diagonal cuts on the ends. This will leave an ⅛-inch gap between each end of the replacement tubing and the original tubing.

Now cut two reinforcing sleeves, sawing straight across (not diagonally) the tubing. For this purpose, select tubing of the same wall thickness as the original, and with an outside diameter equal to the inside diameter of the original tubing. The sleeves should make a snug fit inside the original tubing — clearance between

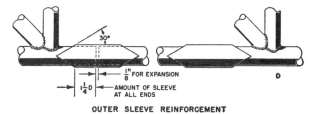

OUTER SLEEVE REINFORCEMENT

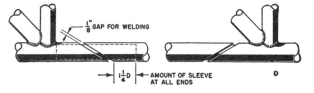

INNER SLEEVE REINFORCEMENT

Figure 3. — Inner and outer sleeve splice.

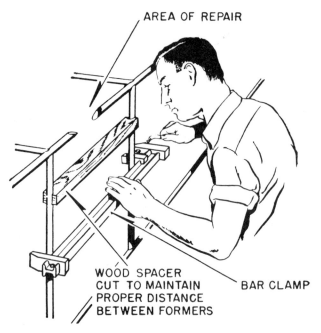

AREA OF REPAIR

WOOD SPACER
CUT TO MAINTAIN
PROPER DISTANCE
BETWEEN FORMERS

BAR CLAMP

Figure 4. — Brace for alining members.

sleeve and tubing should be no more than one sixty-fourth inch. These inner sleeves should be long enough so that either end of a sleeve is not less than 1¼ tube diameters from the original cuts in the original tubing and the replacement tube.

The success of the splicing process depends on following a logical step-by-step procedure, as set forth in the following pages.

Set up a brace arrangement to support the structure while welding. Figure 4 illustrates how a brace replaces the damaged tubing in holding the vertical members in alinement while working.

Dip the replacement tube and inner sleeves into hot Paralketone (about 165° F.), to help prevent corrosion. Wipe the Paralketone from the outside of the replacement tubing and sleeves.

Make a small mark on the outside of each original tube stub end, halfway along the diagonal cut, as shown in figure 5. Then measure off a distance 2¼ diameters long from the nearest end of each diagonal cut on the original tubing. Center-punch the tube at these points and drill No. 40 holes — with the drill held

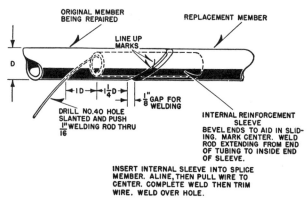

ORIGINAL MEMBER
BEING REPAIRED

REPLACEMENT MEMBER

LINE UP
MARKS

D

1 D   1½D

⅛" GAP FOR WELDING

DRILL NO.40 HOLE
SLANTED AND PUSH
1/16" WELDING ROD THRU

INTERNAL REINFORCEMENT
SLEEVE
BEVEL ENDS TO AID IN SLID-ING. MARK CENTER. WELD ROD EXTENDING FROM END OF TUBING TO INSIDE END OF SLEEVE.

INSERT INTERNAL SLEEVE INTO SPLICE MEMBER. ALINE, THEN PULL WIRE TO CENTER. COMPLETE WELD THEN TRIM WIRE. WELD OVER HOLE.

Figure 5. — How to draw inner sleeves into tubing.

at a 90° angle to the surface of the tubing. When the hole is started so that the drill will not jump out, slant the drill toward the cut and continue at a 30° angle. Remove burrs from the edges of the holes with a ¼-inch drill.

Take a length of 1/16-inch welding or brazing wire, thrust one end through the hole just drilled, and push it out the diagonally cut open end of the original tubing. Repeat this at the other stub end. Use these wires to draw the sleeves into the tubing.

Next, weld the end of each wire protruding from the open end of the tubing to the inside of one of the inner sleeves, as may be seen in figure 5. To help draw the sleeve into the tube, bevel the ends of the sleeves to which the wires are welded.

Make a narrow mark around the center of the reinforcing sleeves.

At this juncture, push the inner sleeves into the replacement tube so that the point where the wire is welded to the sleeve is 180° from the drilled hole. If the drilled hole is at the bottom of the tubing, the inner sleeves are placed so that the point at which the wire is welded is at the top. If the inner sleeve fits too tightly in the replacement tube, chill the sleeve with dry ice or in cold water. If the sleeve persists in sticking, polish it with emery cloth.

Aline the stub ends of the original tube with the replacement tube.

Now begin pulling the end of the wire protruding from the drilled hole. Pull the sleeve along until the center mark on the sleeve is directly in line with the center mark on the diagonal cut. When these marks line up, the sleeve is centered beneath the joint, as shown in figure 5. Repeat this process for the other sleeve at the opposite end of the replacement tube.

Bend the pulling wire over the edge of the hole so as to hold the sleeve in position, and weld the inner sleeve to the original tube stub and replacement tube at one end. This fills the 1/8-inch gap between replacement tube and original tube at one end. After the joint is welded, snip off the pulling wire flush with the surface of the tube and weld over the drilled hole.

Allow this weld to cool, then adjust the brace to provide for contraction and shrinkage. After the brace is adjusted pull the sleeve into position and tack-weld the gap at the other end of the replacement tube. This will hold the joint in alinement. Remove the brace to eliminate any restraint of the contraction forces at this joint, then, finally, complete the weld around the gap previously tack-welded.

The replacement tube should now be welded into place — neatly reinforced with inner sleeves at the joints.

The same general method can be used for any of the other splice methods we will discuss.

A partial replacement tube of the same diameter as the original, reinforced by outside sleeves, is another method of repairing tubing. Since this method requires the greatest amount of welding, there is more danger of distortion from the welding heat generated. Therefore, it is the least desirable of the methods.

There may be occasions, however, when the damage is so located that neither the inner sleeve type of splice nor the larger diameter replacement tube is applicable. In such cases, the outer sleeve type of splice, such as shown in figure 3, is the only alternative.

To accomplish the outside sleeve reinforcement, proceed according to the following step-by-step outline.

First, cut out the damaged section of tubing by sawing straight across, not diagonally, making certain that the cuts are located away from the middle third of the affected area. Then cut a section of replacement tubing which matches the original tubing in diameter, wall thickness, and length.

A gap of not more than one thirty-second inch should exist between the ends of the replacement tubing and the stub ends of the original tubing.

For the outer reinforcement sleeves, select a length of tubing with an inside diameter equal to the outside diameter of the original tubing. A clearance of no more than one sixty-fourth inch should exist between sleeves and tubing.

Saw out the sleeves with either diagonal or fishmouth ends — fishmouth ends are preferable. Make the sleeves long enough so that their nearest ends are 1¼ tube diameters from the ends of the cuts in the original tubing.

File off the burr from the edges of both sleeves and reinforcing tubing, then dip the sections in a bath of hot (165° F.) Paralketone. Wipe off the tube and sleeves, and slip the two sleeves over the replacement tubing. Aline the replacement tubing with the stub ends of the original tubing and push the sleeves along until they are centered over each joint. Rotate them to suit the space and to provide the greatest reinforcement.

Tack weld the two sleeves to the replacement tube in two places, then weld both ends of one sleeve to the replacement tube and original tube. Allow this weld to cool to prevent undue warping before welding around both ends of the other sleeve.

Larger Diameter Replacement Tube

Dispensing with reinforcing sleeves and using a larger diameter replacement tube requires the least amount of cutting and welding. It is thus desirable from the viewpoint of controlling distortion set up by the heat of the welding flame. This technique cannot be used, however, when a tube is damaged too near a cluster joint due to the fact that there will not be a sufficiently long stub end.

Carrying the splice past the joint into the next section of tubing is not recommended because it adds unnecessary weight to the structure. Nor can tubing of larger diameter be used if brackets are mounted on the original tubing. In this latter case, the replacement tub-

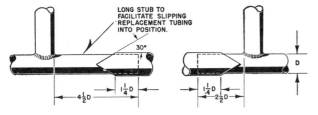

Figure 6. — Larger diameter replacement tube.

ing must be of the same diameter as the original.

When this type of splice is used, cut out the damaged tubing so that a short stub of at least 2½ tube diameters is at one end and a long stub with a length of at least 4½ tube diameters at the other end. The cuts must be outside the middle third, as shown in figure 6.

Cut the replacement tube from a spare length of steel tubing having an inside diameter approximately equal to the outside diameter of the original tubing. The clearance between the two should not exceed one sixty-fourth inch. The fishmouth style of cut is preferable for the ends of the replacement tube.

The replacement tube should be sufficiently long that each end extends at least 1¼ tube diameters past the ends of the original tube.

File the burr from the edges of the replacement tube and the original tube stubs, then dip the replacement tube in hot Paralketone, wiping off the outside of the tube following immersion.

Spring the long stub of the original tube slightly out of normal position so that the replacement tube can be slipped over it. Then pull the replacement tube over the short stub and center it over the cut in the original tubing.

Tack weld one end of the replacement tube in four places, then quarter weld completely around that end. Allow the weld to cool, then weld the other end of the replacement tube to the original tube.

CUT TO A SNUG FIT WITH A RAT-TAIL FILE.

Figure 7. — T-joint.

Tee And Cluster Joints

Joints in which two tubes meet at an angle are quite common in aircraft construction. The simplest and most frequently used joint is the **T-JOINT**, illustrated in figure 7, which usually consists of an auxiliary member welded at right angles to a main or continuous member. If the two members join at an angle other than 90°, they constitute a saddle joint.

Proper construction of the **T-JOINT** involves only a small amount of fitting. This fitting can be done by filing the end of the vertical member to a concave shape and fitting it over the rounded surface of the horizontal member, as shown in figure 7.

Where the tube must be welded in a fixed position — as is likely to be the case when airplane structures

Welded Fitting Details - Acro Sport

Shown are rear landing gear and wing fittings, as well as rear flying wire fittings.

Join and fit landing gear and flying wire fittings prior to forming around the tube and welding.

The front and rear landing gear fitting is shown tacked into position. Note the drill rod which passes through both front and rear fittings to provide proper alignment during welding.

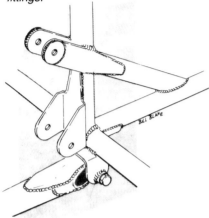

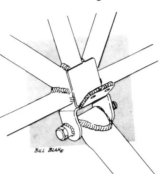

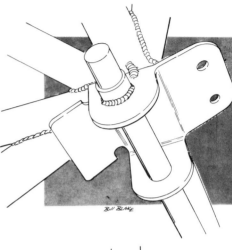

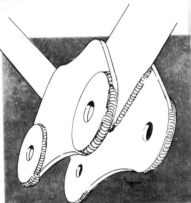

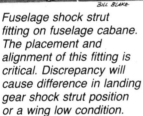

Fuselage shock strut fitting on fuselage cabane. The placement and alignment of this fitting is critical. Discrepancy will cause difference in landing gear shock strut position or a wing low condition.

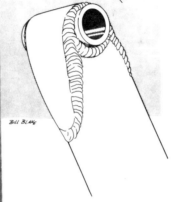

Upper end of front landing gear strut. This end should be completed prior to lower end being jig fitted to axle. A bolt mounted vertically through the bushing will provide accuracy while in the jig.

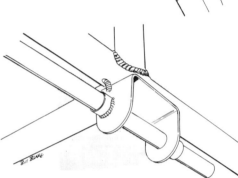

Drill rod used to align front and rear landing gear fittings while tacking into position.

Top fuselage center section cluster joint showing left cabane strut fitting (with bolt), and wire attach lug fitting welded in place.

Front landing gear and double flying wires fitting offers sturdiness.

34

are repaired — a combination of techniques will probably be employed. At some points on the tubing, the backhand method will give the desired control of the puddle, so that thorough fusion can be obtained. In a restricted area, it may be necessary to "dig in" with the torch to secure penetration to the root of the weld, even though this practice is frowned upon in the welding of flat stock.

When a number of tubes are welded at a common joint, the joint is referred to as a CLUSTER JOINT. It is usually composed of a main member, a vertical tube, and other auxiliary tubes at varying angles to the main member. The vertical member is the first one attached. While it may be merely tacked in place, it is usually completely welded because of the additional strength. The other auxiliary members are then carefully fitted into place and welded.

In all cluster joints, the center lines of all members usually converge at a common point. By this precaution, stresses are distributed proportionately upon all members of the joint.

The term quarter welding is a variation of skip welding used to avoid distortion. To perform this technique, first tack weld the tubing joint at four equidistant places, then weld diametrically opposite segments from tack to tack.

Auxiliary Reinforcements

Reinforcements such as gussets, inserts, wrapper gussets, and finger straps are often used in connection with tubular joints, especially the **T** and cluster joints, and in reinforcing clamps, such as those to which the engines are bolted. These reinforcements relieve some of the stresses on the joint itself, and increase the rigidity of the joint.

Gussets

Reinforcement plates in the form of flat gussets are often placed between the members of a cluster or **T**-joint to give added support. This principle is illustrated in figure 8. They are usually triangular in shape, with the legs of equal length.

The thickness of the gusset should be at least equal to the wall thickness of the tubing. It is usually welded on one side only. In many cases, the gusset does not extend into the apex of the angle but is instead notched out a short distance.

There is considerable controversy as to the direction in which the weld should proceed, that is, whether it should begin in the restricted area or go toward it. The factor determining the choice of direction for torch travel is the relative importance of limiting distortion caused by contraction when the weld cools, as opposed to the importance of preventing stress concentration in the joint. For example, if the job being welded is a portion of an engine mount which is not to be heat treated after welding to relieve stresses, welding from the restricted area out is probably more desirable.

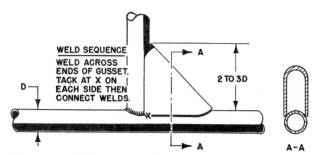

Figure 9. — Wrapper gusset.

If the unit is heat treated after welding to relieve stresses, the stress concentration is compensated for, and is not as important a factor as the prevention of distortion from contraction. It is then common practice to weld the first edge of the gusset in either direction, since the other edge is free to expand except for the tacks, which are placed near the ends of the seam. Welding of the second edge is completed by beginning at a point about one-fourth to one-half inch in from the outer edge of the gusset, and welding out to the edge; the remainder of the bead is then welded from the point near the outer edge to the inner part of the gusset, as explained in figure 8. Overlap the parts of the bead about one-eighth to one-fourth inch to secure thorough fusion. It is not advisable to lift the torch suddenly from the edge of the gusset, as a pinhole is likely to be formed which may serve as a point for the concentration of stresses, leading to failure of the member by cracking. Another recommended practice is to bring the bead around to the end of the gusset, rather than finishing it on the surface of the joint.

Inserts

A great deal of strength can be obtained from the set-up known as the insert. In this procedure, the tubes are slotted and filed to allow a snug fit over the plate which is inserted in the slot. The ends of the tube are filed to a convex shape, then hammered down with a special forming tool. This shaping is performed on both sides of the plate. The point at which an engine mount ring is welded together is quite often a scarf butt with a plate inserted in the joint to give added strength at this point. Inserts are welded on both sides.

Wrapper Gussets And Finger Straps

The WRAPPER GUSSET is really a double gusset. It is made up of a square piece of material with side dimensions similar to those for ordinary gussets, as figure 9 describes.

The main member of any tubular assembly, with an

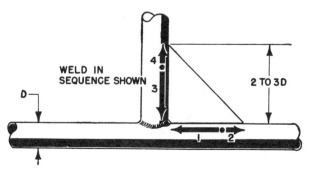

Figure 8. — Principle of and steps in welding the flat gusset.

injury such as a dent at points where truss members terminate, may be repaired by welding a sheet-metal patch over the damaged portion. This repair is known as the formation of FINGER STRAPS. The metal is approximately the same thickness as the tube being repaired. The finger should have a width equal to the diameter of the brace tube, and a length equal to three or four diameters. The ends of finger straps and wrappers should be rounded to prevent the formation of an annealed zone in a straight cross-section of the tube.

Spacing

As noted in the sketches for the various types of tubing joints and splices, there may be two reasons for spacing the ends of tubing. Spacing may be necessary to allow for expansion, as in the case of the ends of the original tube inside the outer sleeve splice. Spacing may also be required to allow penetration, as in the case of the ends of the original tube, where an inner splice is used. Fusion must extend into the inner sleeve, which cannot be accomplished without space between the ends of the outer members.

Penetration

Specifications for penetration will vary with the type of joint used. Butt joints, either plain, scarfed, or fish mouth, should have penetration to the full thickness of the tubing. Lap welds, such as those encountered in the various types of splices, have fusion including 100 percent of the thickness of the outer tube and from 25 to 50 percent of the inner tube. In the T-joint, penetration should extend from 25 to 50 percent of both members.

Appearance Of Bead

Beads may be either concave or convex in shape, depending upon the type of joint and upon the reinforcement required. Beads should be uniform in height and width, the ripples should be well defined and equidistant, and the edge of the bead should be well fused with the surface at all points.

Minor Repairs

Most repairs on aircraft tubing require cutting-out and welding-in of a partial replacement tube, or replacement of an entire new section of tubing. Some repairs, however, are comparatively minor, an example of which is the straightening of a slightly buckled or bent piece of fuselage tubing.

Such repair is relatively simple, and if the part is made of chrome molybdenum in a non-heat-treated condition, it will actually be stronger after having been straightened. This strength is due to the cold-working the metal undergoes during straightening.

The equipment required consists of a steel screw C-clamp, three blocks of hardwood, and a piece of heavy iron beam the same length as the bow, or bend, in the tube. Cut the wood blocks to fit the shape of the tube and line the grooves with leather or canvas. Place

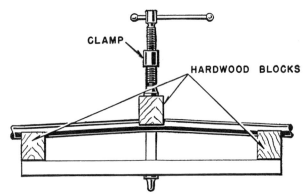

Figure 10. — Straightening a bent piece of tubing.

one of the grooved blocks at either end of the bent section and apply the beam so that it spans the bent area and backs up the two blocks. (Figure 10).

Apply the third block on the opposite side of the tube at the point where the bend is greatest. Slip one end of the C-clamp over the iron beam and tighten the clamp down on the block at the center of the bend.

Tighten the clamp until the tube is bent slightly in the opposite direction, then remove the clamp and the blocks. Check the alinement of the tube by placing an accurate straightedge on both its side and top. If the straightedge check shows that a slight bow remains in the tube, reapply blocks and clamp and repeat the process until the tube lines up with the straightedge in both planes.

If cracks appear at the point where the maximum bend was corrected, drill a hole at the ends of the crack and weld a split sleeve over the crack. In each case where a bent tube is straightened, carefully test all nearby welded joints for cracks. When cracks appear, they must be repaired.

Let us suppose that a small, smooth dent is found in a length of tubing, but the piece is not out-of-round

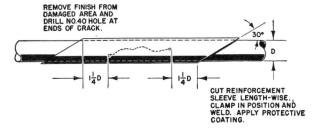

Figure 11. — Cracked-tube reinforcement by means of a split sleeve.

for any considerable length. A simple way of removing the dent is to push it out by air pressure. To accomplish this repair, remove one of the self-tapping screws provided at the ends of the main steel tubes, and apply an air pressure of 75 pounds or more per square inch to the inside of the steel tubing. With a torch, heat the dented area evenly to a dull red until the internal air pressure forces out the dent and restores the original shape of the tube.

If the combined internal air pressure and heat are not sufficient to remove the dent, tack-weld a welding rod to the center of the dent, and pull on the rod while heating the area. When the dent is removed, disconnect the rod, allow the area to cool, and then release the internal air pressure. Finally, replace the self-tapping screw which was removed.

When a crack is discovered in tubing, remove all finish from the area with steel wool or a wire brush. If the crack is located in an original weld bead, carefully chip, file, or grind on the existing weld bead, and reweld over the crack along the original weld line. Do not remove any portion of the existing tube or reinforcing material when grinding off the weld bead.

If the small crack is near a cluster joint but not actually on the weld bead, remove the finish and then drill a No. 40 (0.098) hole at each end to prevent the crack from growing. Then weld an overlapping piece of metal over the area. When the job is completed, apply a coat of zinc chromate primer to the area from which the finish was removed. Finally, apply finish coats to match the adjoining surfaces.

If previous attempts to straighten the tube have caused dents or cracks in its structure, it can be either reinforced· or the damaged part can be cut out and replaced. If the damage is not too serious, reinforce the part by means of a split sleeve without removing the tube. In such event, the reinforcing material should be a piece of tubing having an inside diameter equal to the outside diameter of the damaged tubing. Both tubings should have the same wall thicknesses. Figure 11.

Cut both ends of the reinforcing sleeve diagonally at about a 30° angle. The sleeve should be long enough

to extend a distance of 1¼ tube-diameters past each end of the crack. Cut the reinforcing sleeve in half lengthwise, and separate the half sections. Remove the finish from the surface of the affected area with steel wool for 3 inches on each side of the damage. This done, clamp the two sleeve sections over the damaged area of the original tubing. Weld the two halves of the reinforcing sleeve together and then weld both ends of the sleeve to the damaged tubing.

Welding Problems

What welding rod should be used when welding 4130 steel?

The welding rod you select is the result of several factors; one, will the weldment require heat treating for high strength or only a normalizing or stress relieving? Also, what type of welding method will be applied to the manufacturing of the assembly?

High strength heat-treated parts will require a high strength welding rod. These are:

1. 4130, Cms 32
2. Ox-weld 71B
3. 502

All of these rods will give high strength welds. When heat-treated, these are recommended for high strength areas only and must be handled properly.

For welding the average 4130 assembly (weld stress frams) using gas welding, use Ox-weld 1 or 7 rod. However, DO NOT use these rods if the welding is to be done by TIG welding (heliarc). TIG welding requires a special rod which has a more refined metal that has been produced in a vacuum furnace and has been designed for this process. Ox-weld 65 is such an alloy. It is low in carbon, sulfur, and silicone and is degassed. This rod is readily obtainable. The rod is also available under different trade names and manufacturing companies, but the 65 is the cross reference

number to use when asking for an equivalent type of welding rod. Ox-weld 32 or CMS32 is also acceptable, but aero-space uses the OX 65 welds that will not be heat-treated to more than a stress-relieving temperature. Now that I mention stress-relieving, I must stress the importance of heating 4130 steel after TIG welding. When 4130 is welded by the TIG method, the weld develops a brittle area adjacent to the weld boundary called the heat affected zone (HAZ). This will cause a weld failure if the weldment is not thick combinations of metal joining; for example: engine mounts, landing gear attach points, landing gears, pylon posts for wing attachments.

Post heating of 4130 is not difficult; simply apply heat to the weld joint after welding with an actylene torch, bring the weld and adjacent area to a dull red, 1000 degrees F.; then let cool slowly. As 4130 will harden in the air, keep breezes from cooling the metal.

When 4130 is handled as outlined above, you will have welds that are of the highest integrity, but you must follow the metallurgy rules, or your weldment will not give you the service you need and expect.

The pros and cons of welding 4130 steel are varied, but the above directions and the standard practice of the aero-space industry.

by Maynard Crosby

Aircraft Welding

How to Get Good Results

by Antoni (Tony) Bingelis

The subject is controversial. Should the home-builder try to stress relive his 4130 welded structures with a torch?

The act of stress relieving a weldment is simple, and although highly recommended by many expert welders, it is poopooed (no such word . . . it just sounds right) by others just as well qualified. The treatment requires that the weld, and the metal areas adjacent to it, be heated uniformly with an acetylene torch to bring the metal to a dull red (approximately 1,000°F) condition and then cooled in still air. That's it. Now, why should this be necessary? When steel is heated as in welding, it increases in size in all its dimensions. While the weld is progressing, a rather narrow zone adjacent to it will reach a plastic condition and ultimately a molten state if the heating continues. This uneven heating sets up stresses in the metal. The metal that is further away from the flame will resist the expansion taking place in the weld area. Meanwhile back at the weld, the tremendous initial pressures exerted by the heated metal become less resistant to the surrounding pressures of the cooler metal. The plastic center begins to yeild to the compression force, which is now capable of buckling the plasticized metal in the weld area. This process continues along the line of the weld. And since all of the pressure or stress is not relieved in the process, these stresses remain trapped, or locked-in as the saying goes. Distortion also is a by-product of these complex changes in the metal. As soon as the welding is completed, the molten metal, if it is permitted to do so, begins to cool down, somewhat more rapidly in comparison to the surrounding areas which will not have been heated much. In effect, this uncontrolled cooling causes an uneven contraction in the metal, as the cool metal further from the vicinity of the weld induces a quenching effect. This effect, of course, would even be greater if there were a nearby weld cluster or a welded fitting.

Anyone who has welded an engine mount or other structure requiring the exact alignment and positioning of mounting holes will attest to the fact that, without rigid jigging, the assembly would crawl around during the welding, as if it were alive. Indeed, the expansion of the metal from the heat of welding and its subsequent cooling and contraction are usually so drastic that the builder must allow for the effect of this distortion.

Ordinarily, such stresses are not as severe nor do they present a problem in simple welded joints that are subjected only to static tension, torsion, or compression. No problem that is, provided the metal's ductility has not been seriously impaired by the welding. It is mostly with larger parts that are highly loaded, and perhaps subjected to vibration during their service life that the prospect of cracking or failure of the weld must be faced.

So, we do have something to think about in regard to the locked-in stresses of welding. Is this a serious enough condition to require some form of stress relief, or should it be ignored because the homebuilder is unable to heat treat the entire assembly in a furnace?

Among those who say that the stress relief of a weld with a torch is not necessary or is not recommended, are some very good welders. Undoubtedly, these welders follow a welding procedure much like this — . . . preheat the metal, make the weld, and complete the process by playing the torch over the entire vicinity of the weld until the molten area has cooled down to a red-heat. Then, and only then, is the torch finally withdrawn. What these welders are doing, in effect, is stress relieving the weldment at the same time it is made. That makes good sense. After all, why leave a newly completed weld where the metal is already thoroughly heated without completing the job? Why should it be necessary to return some time later when the weld and the surrounding metal is totally cold? You would only have to start anew by raising the metal's temperature to that dull red condition necessary for the stress relief you wish to obtain.

It is easy to see that essentially the same results are achieved in both instances except that one welder is more experienced and more frugal with his time and energy. I can understand why such a welder would say that he never stress relieves his welds. Nor is there any conflict in my mind with the procedures adopted and practiced by manufacturers and the professional aerospace engineers as well as factory representatives who believe that the best way to stress relieve a welded 4130 structure is not with a torch but in an oven. Can't argue with that logic. But, I guess their stand is primarily based on the opinion that torch stress relieving is undesirable because the area involved may not be uniformly and thoroughly heated. This is possibly true with some builders who do not take the time to switch to a larger welding tip and those who may not be as careful in heating the areas uniformly and methodically. After all, its easy to inadvertently get some places too hot.

In real life, however, finding an oven to stress relieve an entire fuselage is like finding the pot at the end of the rainbow. So, the option remains, either to stress relieve the completed welds with a torch or to modify the welding technique to assure that the classic pre-

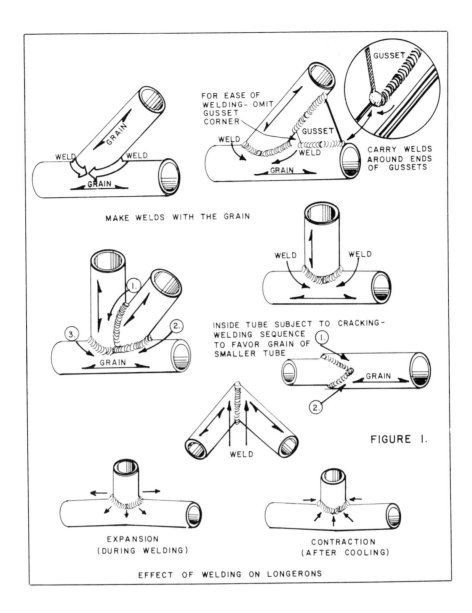

FOR EASE OF WELDING— OMIT GUSSET CORNER

GUSSET

WELD

WELD

GRAIN

GUSSET

CARRY WELDS AROUND ENDS OF GUSSETS

GRAIN

WELD

WELD

GRAIN

MAKE WELDS WITH THE GRAIN

WELD

WELD

GRAIN

INSIDE TUBE SUBJECT TO CRACKING— WELDING SEQUENCE TO FAVOR GRAIN OF SMALLER TUBE

GRAIN

WELD

FIGURE I.

EXPANSION (DURING WELDING)

CONTRACTION (AFTER COOLING)

EFFECT OF WELDING ON LONGERONS

heat, weld, and post heat applications serve to accomplish the same end result.

Recently, someone tried to convince me that when one attempts to stress relieve a weldment with an acetylene torch (as opposed to using an oven) he simply moves the stresses outward from the welded area, but does not relieve them. That argument concluded with the observation that it would therefore, be more desirable to have these stresses in a welded cluster where the structure was the strongest as opposed to moving them outward on the tubing where the structure was weakest. I don't know why but the remark was added . . . "this, of course, is based on the assumption that 4130 steel was being used in a properly designed structure."

I find that supposition faulty for the most part. It might be true if there were some sort of heat sink a short distance away from the weld which might have a quenching effect on an unevenly heated weldment. However, it seems that during a properly executed stress relief effort this would not be true. Here's why. The weld area is thoroughly pre-heated and brought

up to a dull red condition and, therefore, the heated areas of the metal will range outward to an almost red, very hot, hot, not so hot, to a relatively cool and ultimately cool condition some distance away from the weld. How could such a gradual thermal change in the metal from the weldment to the remainder of the metal cause serious stresses to be moved further outward on the tube as these folks suggest? Again, an exception might be if there were an adjacent welded cluster that was not included in the heating process.

The fact remains that peope who obviously have much experience in this area do honestly disagree on this particular point. Maybe the real disagreement is not so much whether to stress relieve or not, but with the technique utilized in making welds.

Other Matters Involving Stress In Welds

The Matter of pre-heating — What is the best way to begin a weld in 4130 steel? Certainly, not with a concentrated application of the flame directly to the joint. Such a modus operandi (that's Texas talk for . . .

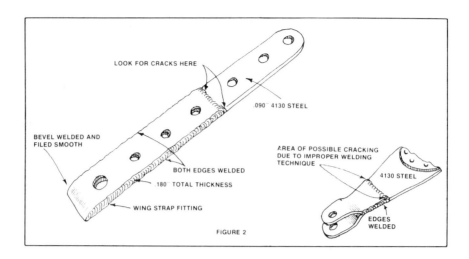

FIGURE 2

technique) may result in committing certain critical welds to a short-lived future even though a fairly good looking uniform weld was obtained. Additionally, a welding procedure like that introduces internal stresses in the adjoining metal in the manner discussed earlier.

The proper starting procedure is to always take the time to pre-heat the metal before starting to weld. The work should be approached with the flame in a playful manner, if you will, playing the flame over the entire area until it is evenly heated. This pre-heating is especially important when there is a nearby welded joint. It doesn't mean though, that the surrounding metal must be raised to a red hot condition . . . not at all.

Weld With the Grain? — Metal does have grain, you know. Somewhat like that in wood. It results from the manufacturing process and is a factor to consider whenever bending metal or welding it. The grain in tubing is noticeable and runs the length of the tube in straight lines. The grain in flat steel stock is likewise visible to the eye and is further delineated by the orientation of the lines of painted specification numbers and letters across the sheet.

Experience has shown that cracks tend to develop in welds made against the grain. Therefore, whenever possible welds should be made in the direction of the grain and not against it.

Examples shown in Figure 1 illustrate several examples of this little heeded peculiarity.

Protect the Weld Against Oxidation — Once the metal is heated to a molten state and the welding puddle forms, air should not be permitted to reach the white hot metal at any time. Use the outer envelope of the flame as a protective blanket against oxidation. This protective blanket must not ever by totally removed even when changing to a new welding rod or readjusting the flame. Certainly, not until the weld is completed and the heated metal has been allowed to cool down to a red heat.

End the Weld Properly — Do not immediately withdraw the torch and marvel at the good looking weld you just completed. Instead, take your time and play the flame over the completed weld area until it cools to a red heat condition. The gradual withdrawal of the heat after the weld is completed minimizes the likelihood of cracks developing, or more likely, the appear-

ance of small pin holes in the cooling puddles where the welds terminate. Furthermore, this procedure improves the ductility of the weld and minimizes the quenching effect the adjacent cooler metal may have. If all this seems familiar to you by now, I would hope so.

Beware of Breezes — Those gentle caressing breezes drifting through your workshop during those hot sultry summer days may be great for you, but they are bad for your welding. When welding 4130 steel do not expose it to any cooling by air in motion. This is an air hardening steel and it will develop cracks when subjected to any sudden cooling, however gentle it might feel to you. That means you should close any door near the welding area and shut off those fans, too, while you are welding. For that matter, you better make sure that your dog doesn't wag his tail, either.

Paul Poberezny fits tubing on landing gear of the Acro Sport I, a fully aerobatic sport biplane he designed. This single place aircraft - and a later two place Acro II - became very popular with homebuilders.

How to Flatten Tubing Ends

Here is something for the antique and biplane enthusiasts. Flattening the tube ends for struts and other applications is a very simple process. The tubes get flattened . . . but in some cases the results are very poor.

The biggest defects are in the sharp mark-off creases left by the jaws of the vise during the forming operation and cracks due to trying to cold work the tubing.

Procedure

Insert forming jaws in the vise.
Heat the tubing cherry red.
Insert tube end and squeeze in the vise.
Trim and weld end as desired.
Reheat tubing end to cherry red condition.
Allow tubing to cool in still air.
Drill end as needed. Tube is ready for use.

Sometimes it is necessary to flatten the tube end asymmetrically due to structural clearance requirements or design. This is just as simple an operation. In this case it is necessary to replace one of the forming jaws with a longer piece of angle iron which serves as a back-up during the squeezing process. This is illustrated in the following drawing.

Procedure in flattening tubing from one side (asymmetrically) is the same as described for the symmetrical flattening. If you try to do this work without heating the tubing to a cherry red condition . . . it will crack along the edges.

by Tony Bingelis

Forming Jaws
Angle Iron ⅛" x 1½"
Make two

Bench Vise

Symmetrically flattened
tube end

Back-up Bar
(Angle Iron)

End welded
(Typical)

Welding Small Tubing Pieces

Many times, while building my aircraft, I was confronted with a problem of welding a short piece of tubing for a bushing or attachment or whatever. But, the problem is always the same in regard to burning a notch in the small piece where the weld comes close to the edge.

So, I found that by either using a bolt or a piece of scrap tubing, with a few thousandths clearance, and sticking this into the small piece to be welded, I can weld right up to the edge without burning away the short tube.

The tube or bolt that's inserted can be quite sloppy, as its main purpose is to absorb heat. It does this better if it is in contact with the tube to be welded, but it doesn't have to be.

Another method of accomplishing this is to weld on a piece that is too long, and then saw it off to size. However, I find that on building up an assembly on the job, I can't always do this as there isn't enough room to get into the area to saw the excess off.

by Ran Reid

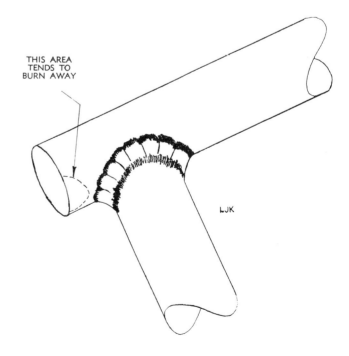

THIS AREA
TENDS TO
BURN AWAY

LJK

Corben Super Ace, a popular homebuilt of the 30s, is recreated and modernized by Paul Poberezny. Note outrigger type landing gear arrangement - a design quite popular in the 30s. Vertical tube on gear is temporary - finished gear will have hydraulic or spring type shock strut mounted in this position.

Techniques For Nonferrous Metals

Aircraft Metals

In everyday language, nonferrous metal means a metal not made from iron ore. The most important of the nonferrous metals in aircraft construction are the aluminum alloys. Others are the magnesium alloys, the nickel-based alloys, and inconel and monel, although the latter two are not strictly nonferrous metals.

Aircraft are composed chiefly of these metals because they are strong and light.

Welding of aluminum alloys in modern aircraft repair has been reduced to a very small portion of the total repair required to maintain the plane. Welding, with few exceptions, is limited to the repair of metal fuel and oil tanks, cowling, cast fittings, or cast motor parts in some of the older types of planes.

Aluminum

Commercially pure aluminum is a silver-white, lustrous metal noted for its lightness — it is only about one-third as heavy as steel. It has a high degree of resistance to corrosion and can be readily formed into intricate shapes.

Aluminum is the most widely distributed of all the elements, next to oxygen and silicon. It is present in all common rocks, but is difficult to extract. Aluminum metal is produced by electrolyzing alumina, which is prepared by purifying bauxite — a hydrated oxide of aluminum containing iron oxide and silicon as the principal impurities. Bauxite deposits of satisfactory quality are distributed throughout the world, and alumina of high purity can be obtained cheaply from these deposits.

In order to electrolyze an aluminum compound, it is necessary to dissolve it in a substance which does not react with aluminum and which is more resistant than aluminum oxide to electrolytic decomposition. Cryolite, a double fluoride of sodium and aluminum, is such a substance. Cryolite melts at about 1,830° F. and, when molten, dissolves about 16 percent of its weight of alumina. By electrolyzing a molten bath of cryolite and aluminum oxide with a current of low voltage and high amperage (aluminum oxide is disassociated into aluminum and oxygen) the molten aluminum, being heavier at 1,850° F. than the molten cryolite, settles to the bottom of the bath. Powdered alumina is added from time to time to replace that electrolyzed. The molten metal is removed by tapping and is poured into molds to solidify as pigs. The metal produced has an average purity of 99.5 percent, which is known as commercially pure aluminum.

One virtue not possessed by pure aluminum is that of strength, and aircraft parts must of necessity be strong as well as light. Aluminum manufacturers have met this problem by adding one or more other metals to the pure aluminum to develop alloys which are both light and strong.

These alloys, available in either cast or wrought forms, can be made still stronger and harder by work-hardening — that is, by rolling, forming, pressing, or otherwise cold-working the metal. Since the hardness

depends on the amount of cold work performed, some of the wrought-aluminum alloys are available in several work-hardened tempers — either ¼ hard, ½ hard, ¾ hard, or hard. The ½ hard temper of aluminum sheet is that most often used for aircraft parts.

To add still greater strength, aluminum alloys are heat-treated, a process of controlled heating and cooling of the metal. With but minor exceptions, aluminum alloys used for structural members in aircraft are heat-treated. The principal aluminum alloy thus used is 24S.

Some of the other heat-treatable alloys used for structural parts of aircraft are A51S, 17S, 53S, 61S, and 25S. These code numbers refer to the kind and

Table 1. — Approximate Size Of Tips And Relative Gas Pressures Used In Welding Varying Thicknesses Of Aluminum

Metal thickness (B&B gage)	Oxyacetylene		
	Diameter of tip orifice (inches)	Oxygen pressure (p. s. i.)	Acetylene pressure (p. s. i.)
24-22	0.025	1	1
20-18	.035	1	1
16-14	.055	2	2
12-10	.065	3	3
⅛-³⁄₁₆	.075	4	4
¼	.085	5	5
⁵⁄₁₆	.085	5	5
⅜	.095	6	6
⅝	.105	7	7

amount of alloying metals which are added to the aluminum to give it certain qualities of strength and hardness. The total amount of alloying elements is seldom more than 6 percent in the wrought forms. Cast forms, however, may contain somewhat higher percentages of alloying metals.

Non-heat-treatable alloys used for parts in aircraft which are not subjected to great stress, such as tanks and fuel lines, include 2S, 3D, 4S, and 52S. A cast alloy, 43, is used for many nonstructural fittings.

In general, very little welding of aluminum aircraft parts is done, because the great majority of them are made of heat-treated metal.

An aircraft welder is not permitted to weld structural parts made of heat-treated aluminum alloys. Even if facilities are available for reheat-treating these parts after welding, it is still not possible to increase the strength of the weld enough to stand up to the stresses which these parts must bear. Remember, the use of torch welding in aircraft is limited to places where high unit stresses are not involved and, consequently, where heat-treated metal is not used.

One common application of torch welding on aircraft aluminum and aluminum alloys is in welding tanks. Torch welding is the simplest method of obtaining gastight or liquidtight seams in such tanks.

General Welding Principles

In oxyacetylene welding the standard torch, hose, and regulators are suitable for both wrought and cast aluminum workpieces.

As in welding any other metal, the first step is that of cleaning the joint, either mechanically or chemically.

To clean the joint mechanically, use a wire brush, steel wool, or abrasive cloth on the edges to be joined until a dull-white, nonreflecting surface is obtained. Be careful not to scratch the metal beyond the weld area, as such scratches are entry points for cracks and corrosion. If considerable corrosion exists, the joint should be chemically cleaned by dipping it from 10 to 30 seconds in a hot solution of 10 percent caustic soda or 10 percent trisodium phosphate, followed by a rinse in a dilute 10 percent nitric acid solution and a final hot-water bath.

After cleaning and otherwise preparing the joint, preheat the piece. A slight preheating of thin sheet is all that is required, and this is accomplished by passing the flame back and forth across the weld area three or four times. Aluminum sheets three-eighths inch or thicker, as well as larger aluminum castings, should be preheated to from 700° to 800° F. When sufficiently preheated, the piece will have lost its metallic ring when struck lightly with another piece of metal.

Preheating avoids heat strains and reduces the amount of welding gas necessary to fuse the seam. Such preheating is imperative because aluminum conducts heat and expands very readily. Castings in particular require careful preheating to prevent serious cracking. Small castings may be preheated with the torch, but larger ones require furnace treatment.

Never preheat aluminum alloys to a temperature higher than 800° F., because the heat may melt some of the alloys and result in burned metal.

Rod Selection

Choosing the proper filler rod is as important with aluminum as with any other metal. Non-heat-treated 2S and 3S require a 2S filler rod. For 52S, 53S, and 61S, a filler rod containing 95 percent aluminum and 5 percent silicon (43S is the code number) is recommended.

Welding rods are available in 1/16-, 1/8-, 3/16-, and 1/4-inch diameters. The usual rule is to match the size rod to the thickness of the base metal.

Welding Tips

Since aluminum is an excellent conductor of heat, it is wise to select a welding tip of a size slightly larger than that used for steel of the same thickness to obtain sufficient heat to melt the base metal. Table 1 shows the recommended sizes of tips and amounts of gas pressure for welding aluminum of varying thicknesses.

The welding flame for aluminum work should be adjusted to neutral. Some welders prefer a slight excess of acetylene in the flame, but experience has shown that a neutral flame — one-to-one mixture of oxygen and acetylene — will serve best. The flame should be soft, which requires adjustment of the torch needle valves so that the gas mixture comes into the tip at low speed.

Flux

Aluminum or aluminum alloys, when exposed to the air for any length of time, will form a thin film of oxide on their surfaces which is troublesome to the welder for two reasons — the oxide has a higher melting point than the metal, and it prevents the free flow of molten metal.

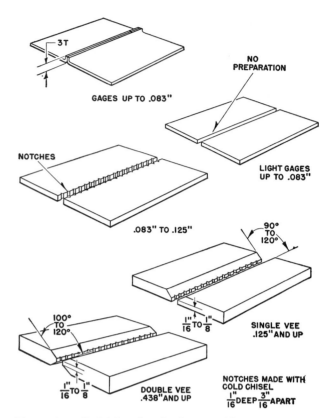

Figure 1. — Butt joints for aluminum welding.

The most satisfactory method of removing oxides is through the use of a flux, the application of which does several important things. Its chemical action reduces the melting point of the oxide below that of the metal, and it dissolves some of the oxide and floats it to the surface, thus preventing oxide formation.

Flux for aluminum generally comes in powder form, and is usually mixed with water to form a thin paste (two parts of flux to one part water).

Unless the particular job requires a filler rod, paint the flux directly into the joint. If a filler rod is used, coat it with flux. On thick sections of aluminum, both the metal and the filler rod are treated with flux.

Joint Design

Aluminum may be welded in any of the joint designs; however, butt joint welds on sheet aluminum alloy should be of the flange type, and such joints should be clamped together and tack-welded to hold them in alinement. Tacks are placed at intervals of from 1 1/4 to 1 1/2 inches apart, following the same proce-

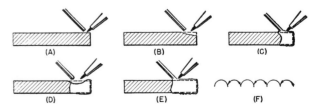

Figure 2. — Proper filler rod motion in welding sheet aluminum.

dure as for stainless steel. Principles of aluminum butt-joint welding are illustrated in figure 1.

An ordinary butt joint, such as shown in figure 1, may be used when the piece is less than 0.083-inch in thickness. Heavier sheets should be notched. Edges of the joint are notched with a cold chisel to a depth of about one-sixteenth inch. Spaced three-sixteenth inch apart, these notches act as expansion joints and also aid the flux in thoroughly penetrating into the seam.

Welding Procedure

The welding of aluminum requires particular attention to a few of the factors involved in the process, the remaining factors being the same as in the welding of other metals. Items requiring this special attention include correct flame adjustment, tacking methods, and torch and rod technique.

Hold the torch at a considerable slant so that it will not blow holes through the metal. An angle of about 45° to the surface of the base metal is just about right for butt joints. In welding a **T**-joint, the flame is held midway between the two pieces. The inner cone of the flame should be about one-eighth inch from, but never touching, the metal.

Exercise considerable care in evenly heating both edges of the joint so that the heat will be well spread around in the weld area. Do not hold the torch too long in one spot — aluminum conducts heat so well that the entire area around the weld will crumble and fall away.

Another thing to remember is HOT SHORT — that is, when aluminum approaches its melting temperature, it loses its power of adhesion and cannot support its own weight. If care is not exercised, the puddle may drop through the metal or cracks may develop from strains set up in the weld area.

If filler rod is used, be careful to see that the filler metal enters the weld only where the base metal has been brought to a molten state.

The problem of deciding exactly when the edges have reached their melting point is complicated, in the case of aluminum welding, by the fact that no visible color change occurs when the melting point is reached. The aluminum may be solid one instant and then, with no change in appearance other than a quick wrinkling and shrinking action, melt and sag.

Aluminum begins to feel soft and elastic just before melting takes place. The instant that this feel indicates approach of the melting point, dip the filler rod into the puddle and permit it to alloy with the metal. A diagram illustrating the dipping motion the filler rod should take as the weld progresses is presented in figure 2.

In (A) of figure 2, the metal is being heated; in (B), melting of the base metal has begun; (C) shows the filler rod dipped into the molten puddle and allowed to melt; and in (D), the filler rod is lifted while the torch flame is moved forward to continue the melting process. The filler rod dipping procedure is shown being repeated in (E), and (F) illustrates the continuous dipping motion of the filler rod as the weld progresses along the seam.

In the dipping process described in figure 2, never lift the rod out of the flame envelope. As the welding process nears the end of the seam, increase the speed of progress to prevent a collapse of the base metal.

In welding sheet or plate, it is an excellent practice to begin near the center of the pieces and weld toward the ends. This procedure better controls expansion and contraction and will prevent, in most instances, the cracking that often occurs when the weld is begun at the very end of a sheet.

Welds on both aluminum sheet and plate should be done with one pass of the welding torch.

Wash all traces of flux from the surfaces of the completed weld. Otherwise, if moisture is present, the elements in the flux will attack the base metal and cause corrosion. To remove the flux, scrub the piece with a stiff brush and hot water. If the weld is difficult to reach with a brush, submerge the piece in a cold 10-percent sulphuric acid bath until all traces of flux have been removed, then wash the piece in fresh, running water to remove the acid.

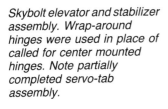
Skybolt elevator and stabilizer assembly. Wrap-around hinges were used in place of called for center mounted hinges. Note partially completed servo-tab assembly.

Front quartering view of the widened Junior Ace fuselage with its distinctive outrigger landing gear. Wings attach to the square tubes on top of the cabane struts while four holes in front fuselage bay mate with the tubular engine mount.

Steel Tube Fuselages

Factors for Economy in Fabrication and Assembly

Particularly adapted to smaller types of aircraft is the welded steel tube type of fuselage. This form of construction permits fabricating the fuselage, the basic structural element of the airplane, in simple, accessible jigs, and makes it possible to apply the fuselage skin or covering as the last step in the assembly of the airplane.

The purely abstract considerations involved in the design of welded steel tube structures are identical to those common to other phases of structural engineering. The stress analysis methods applicable to steel tube fuselages are but modifications of the established procedure used for analyzing bridge trusses and similar structures. After the directions and magnitudes of the loads involved are known, and the required margins of safety established, the determination of tube sizes and joint requirements become comparatively simple matters. The tubes can be joined by welding with either the electric arc or gas. The process differs from other applications of welding only in that greater skill is required in working with thin tube gages to maintain required accuracy in alignment.

When laying out a welded steel tube fuselage it is of prime importance that the designer have a practical knowledge of all the factors affecting the economical production of the structure. These factors begin to influence the layout of the basic structure at the time when it is simply a geometrical concept of lines and points, and continue to shape the design throughout to the determination of major attachment fittings, selection of the method of covering the tube structure, and finally of detail fittings and attachment points required for controls and equipment. If these factors are neglected anywhere in the progress of the design, beginning with the geometric layout of the basic structure and concluding with the design of the last attachment fitting, the fundamental economy of welded steel tube structures will be sacrificed.

In the design of a welded steel tube fuselage the first step is the determination of the fuselage form to be used. The basic fuselage structure may consist of two main forms: the all-steel-tube structure wherein the complete primary structure is a welded steel tube truss, or the so-called "composite" structure made by joining together a welded steel tube foward portion which includes the cockpits, and an aluminum-alloy semi-monocoque aft structure.

Some builders favor the all-steel-tube design, be-

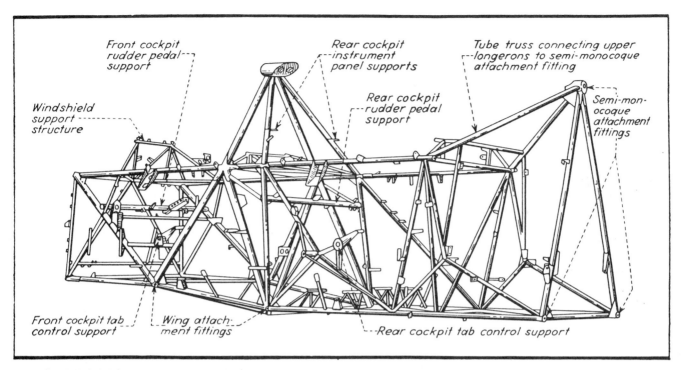

Front cockpit rudder pedal support

Windshield support structure

Rear cockpit instrument panel supports

Rear cockpit rudder pedal support

Tube truss connecting upper longerons to semi-monocoque attachment fitting

Semi-monocoque attachment fittings

Front cockpit tab control support

Wing attachment fittings

Rear cockpit tab control support

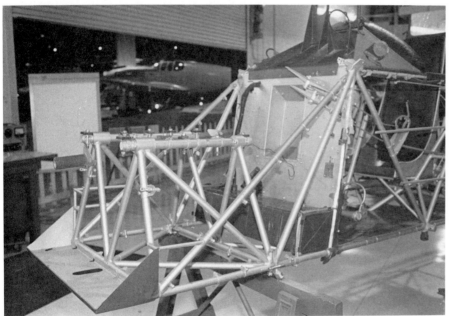

Above - Typical World War II era steel tube structure for a composite-type fuselage incorporating a steel tube forward section, joined to an aluminum alloy semi-monocoque aft section of a two-place tandem training aircraft. Note the many attachments added to the basic load carrying tube structure.

Rugged construction of typical 20s era military trainer is evident in the size and number of tubes involved in this Consolidated PT-1. In those days they did not have 4130 steel — not to mention the abuse inflicted by heavy handed students! The PT-1 fuselage shown left is an original on loan from the Air Force Museum. It serves as a pattern for a part original/part replica flyable aircraft under construction by the EAA Air Museum's Restoration Shop. Note heavy duty engine mount. A Hisso will be installed.

Fuselage structure of a Steen Skybolt. Lots of welding completed, but a good share yet to go with stand-offs, numerous tabs, and other fixtures to be welded later to the basic fuselage.

lieving that a single fabrication process throughout for the basic structure facilitates production by simplifying tooling, and eliminating the fittings necessary for attachments of the semi-monocoque section. This form is also desirable because access panels extending the full length of the fuselage are removable thus providing ample room for installation operations during the airplane assembly. The panels can also be removed for inspection and service.

Other builders believe that complete access to the extreme aft portion of the fuselage is rarely required. They prefer the composite type in order to take advantage of its lighter weight, and the economy gained by eliminating the necessity of fairing side panels and their supports to the aft portion of the fuselage.

Regardless of the type selected, however, there are certain factors involving the basic geometry of the tube structure layout which must not be neglected.

Consider the all-steel-tube structure first. Because of the need for cockpit spaces, landing gear and upper or lower wing attachment points, the four longeron type structure is almost always used.

The four longeron tube type of structure inherently provides the builder with a choice of any two of the four sides as major sub-assemblies. The practice of dividing the structure into fore and aft sections is universally followed to save weight by reducing tube sizes in the rear section. In cabin type airplanes it is also necessary to build an irregularly shaped front section because of passenger compartment space requirements, with the result that the structure is divided aft of the cabin to permit economical weight distribution, and to simplify tooling, as well as to facilitate final alignment of the tube structure.

Naturally, they include two longerons and the tubes connecting same, a choice must be made to build either the top and bottom frames or the side frames, as sub-assemblies. The forward section bottom frame is usually well braced and may be depended upon to hold its shape and resist distortion through the major assembly. The top frame, however, is usually poorly adapted to retaining its shape as a sub-assembly panel, because of the necessity of providing clear unobstructed bays for cockpits in open cockpit airplanes. At the open bays deflection of the frame may occur after removal of the frame from the sub-assembly jig.

After a consideration of these factors it is logical to design the side frames as sub-assemblies, consisting of the upper and lower longerons, inter-connecting tubes and fittings. A further advantage is obtained in that the sides are usually symmetrically braced so that welding distortion and shrinkage are practically the same for both sides when consistent welding procedures are followed. With proper guidance and indexing the side frames, being well braced, may be depended upon to determine accurately the final structure assembly, thus eliminating the need of an elaborate final assembly jig.

The Pratt truss is shown in all of the fuselage layouts illustrated in this article as this type of truss offers the advantages of normal vertical lines to work from during drafting and tooling layout. However, the Warren truss will usually consist of fewer tubes, and for this reason may be lighter for a given fuselage size. The type of truss used will actually depend upon the required attachment points as governed by factors extraneous to the tube geometry, such as placement of the wing to obtain the correct airplane balance.

Geometry of All-Steel Tube Fuselages

In the line drawings of tube layouts in Figs. 1 to 6 are shown logical development of the geometry of an all-steel-tube fuselage design. The sequence of these figures is based upon the design's desirability from the standpoints of fabrication and tooling, beginning with Fig. 1 as the most desirable. All illustrations are for a fuselage suitable for a two-place, tandem, open-cockpit airplane, but the principles discussed are applicable to all types and therefore detail treatment of the cabin-type airplane has been omitted purposely. Note that in all designs the object is to accomplish the same result, namely to retain all frames in true flat planes whenever possible especially the side frame.

All-steel-tube structure that is ideally adapted for easy and economical construction. From the plan view in Fig. 1, it can be seen that both the upper and the lower longerons of the forward section are perfectly straight in all planes, and are also parallel to and equidistant from the centerline of the airplane for the entire length of this section. The upper and lower longerons of the aft section lie in vertical planes, with the bend in the longerons at a position adjacent to the welded junction of the forward and aft sections. All

longerons are straight lines excepting where the bends occur at the junction just forward of the splice. Also note that these bends are at the same station in both the plan view and the side elevation, and because of this fact the necessary tooling and production operations connected with this fuselage can be readily accomplished.

Upper longerons in the side elevation, Fig. 2, are straight and parallel to centerline of thrust. In the lower longerons one bend is at the same station as the bend in the plan view, another bend is at an intermediate station further forward. If possible, one section of the forward lower longerons should be parallel to the centerline of thrust. In the plan view longerons are straight, equidistant from and also parallel to the airplane's centerline. Upper and lower longerons of aft section lie in a vertical plane. All longerons with the exception of the lower forward are straight between junction points. All of the side frames are in one plane.

Fuselage in which the upper and the lower longerons are straight in the plan view of the front section, shown in Fig. 3, with the exception of the one bend at the station forward of the junction of the forward and

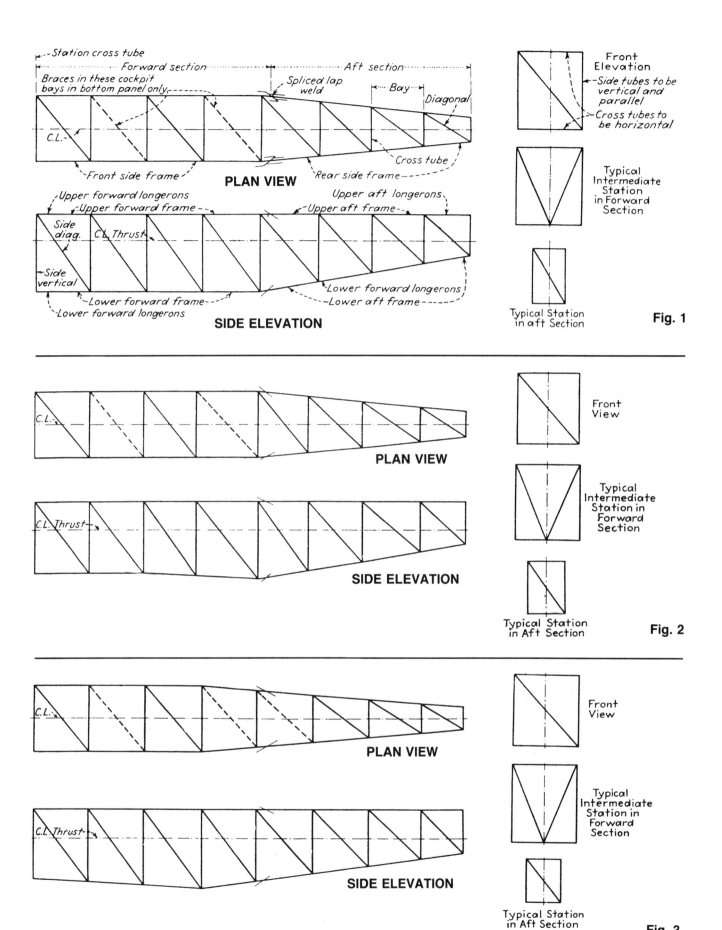

Front Elevation
—Side tubes to be vertical and parallel
—Cross tubes to be horizontal

Typical Intermediate Station in Forward Section

Typical Station in aft Section

Fig. 1

Station cross tube
Forward section
Aft section
Braces in these cockpit bays in bottom panel only
Spliced lap weld
Bay
Diagonal
C.L.
Front side frame
Rear side frame
Cross tube

PLAN VIEW

Upper forward longerons
Upper forward frame
Upper aft longerons
Upper aft frame
Side diag.
C.L. Thrust
Side vertical
Lower forward frame
Lower forward longerons
Lower forward longerons
Lower aft frame

SIDE ELEVATION

Front View

Typical Intermediate Station in Forward Section

Typical Station in Aft Section

Fig. 2

C.L.

PLAN VIEW

C.L. Thrust

SIDE ELEVATION

Front View

Typical Intermediate Station in Forward Section

Typical Station in Aft Section

Fig. 3

C.L.

PLAN VIEW

C.L. Thrust

SIDE ELEVATION

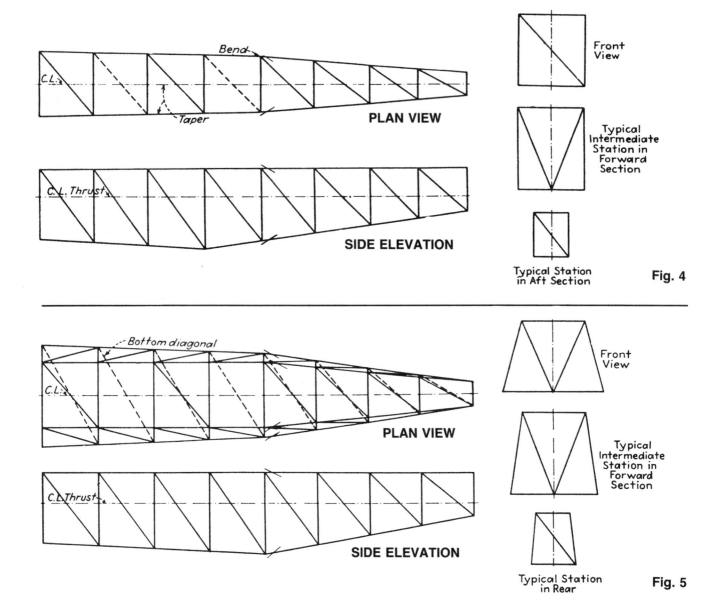

PLAN VIEW

Bend

C.L.

Taper

SIDE ELEVATION

C.L. Thrust

Front View

Typical Intermediate Station in Forward Section

Typical Station in Aft Section

Fig. 4

PLAN VIEW

Bottom diagonal

C.L.

SIDE ELEVATION

C.L.Thrust

Front View

Typical Intermediate Station in Forward Section

Typical Station in Rear

Fig. 5

the aft sections. The aft portions of the forward longerons falls on a straight line with the aft section longerons. The front and the rear sections have vertical sides. In the side elevation the upper longerons are perfectly straight for the length of the fuselage. They are also parallel to the centerline of the thrust. One bend is made in the lower longerons, it is located at the same station at which the bend occurs in the plan view.

Layout of fuselage similar to that in Fig. 3, but not quite as well adapted to construction is shown in Fig. 4. Although sides are vertical, they taper in toward the rear, starting at the front station. The welded junction of fore and aft sections is at the identical station for all longerons. This type of construction introduces some difficulties. Drafting becomes complicated since tubes will be encountered in many layouts that are not in plane of the paper, and must be projected to obtain true views.

Upper longerons in plan view in the forward section, Fig. 5, are straight and parallel to centerline of

airplane; lower longerons are also straight but not parallel with upper ones, being tapered in toward the aft end so that side frames are in a "twisted" plane that complicates all layout and construction. The same condition exists with regard to longerons in the aft section. In side view upper longerons are perfectly straight, and parallel to line of thrust and thus present the only truly unbroken plane in the fuselage, but unfortunately one that cannot be built up as a sub-assembly because of the unbraced cockpit openings, precluding the necessary rigidity. A design of this nature should be avoided because of the complexity involved.

Geometry of Composite-Type Tubular Fuselages

Composite-type fuselages shown in Figs. 6 and 7, are advanced developments wherein the steel-tube structure terminates immediately aft of the rear cockpit, and the aft portion of the fuselage is formed by an aluminum-alloy semi-monocoque structure. (The 'Little Toot; a popular single place biplane that was introduced to homebuilders in the late 50's is an example of this type construction). A composite type fuselage may employ any one of the basic steel tube layouts shown in Figs. 1 to 5, although it is quite obvious that it is still important to use a simple tube structure. The major additional consideration lies in the method of attachment used between steel tube structure and semi-monocoque structure.

Three-point attachment design for connecting a steel tube truss structure to a semi-monocoque section similar to the type that is illustrated in Fig. 6 is considered by airplane designers to be the most practical, since this method of construction permits placing the attachment fittings in favorable position such that much of the torsion and the bending resistance which is inherent in the semi-monocoque type of structure can be utilized to good advantage, which is to say, that these attachment points are placed as wide apart as possible in the structure thus obtaining a particularly favorable result, the achievement of structural strength with good weight economy. The benefits derived from this three-point method of attaching a semi-monocoque structure,

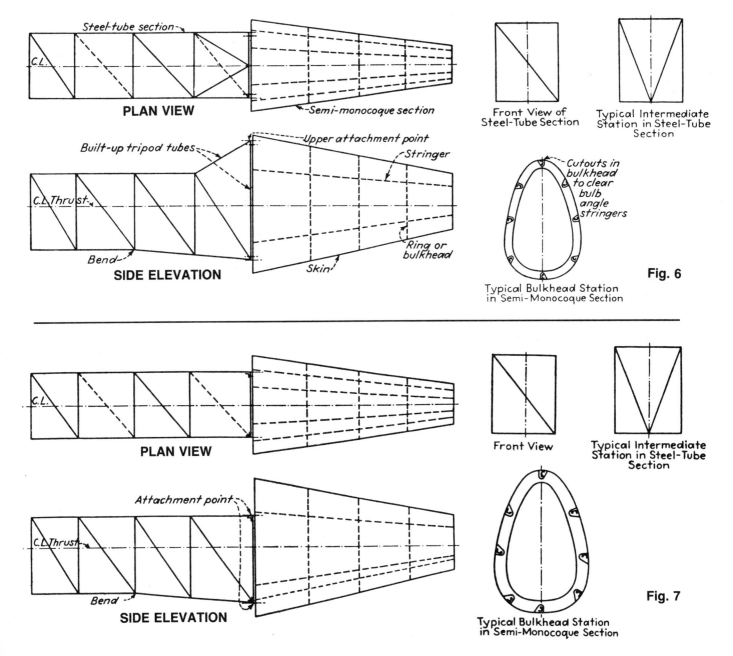

PLAN VIEW — Steel-tube section — C.L. — Semi-monocoque section

SIDE ELEVATION — Built-up tripod tubes — Upper attachment point — Stringer — C.L.Thrust — Bend — Skin — Ring or bulkhead

Front View of Steel-Tube Section

Typical Intermediate Station in Steel-Tube Section

Cutouts in bulkhead to clear bulb angle stringers

Typical Bulkhead Station in Semi-Monocoque Section

Fig. 6

PLAN VIEW — C.L.

SIDE ELEVATION — Attachment point — C.L.Thrust — Bend

Front View

Typical Intermediate Station in Steel-Tube Section

Typical Bulkhead Station in Semi-Monocoque Section

Fig. 7

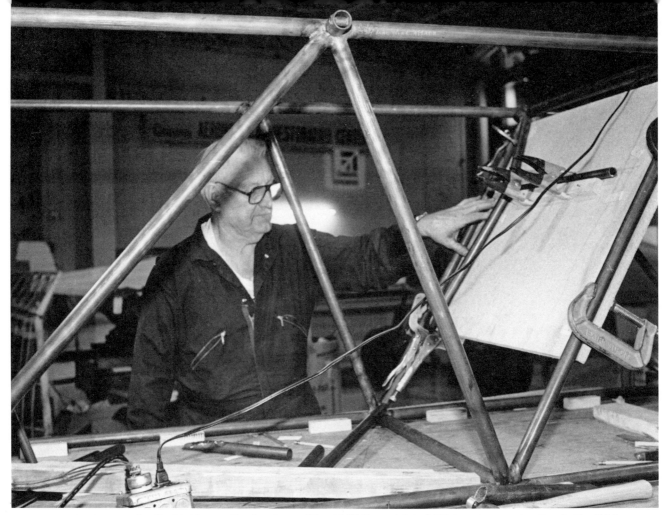

Lloyd Toll checks over the fit of tubing on the fuselage of the 1927 Consolidated PT-1 under construction in the EAA Foundation's restoration center workshop.

however, are offset somewhat by a slight disadvantage in that a separate sub-assembly is required for the triangular tube truss which connects the longerons to the upper semi-monocoque fitting.

Alternative method of semi-monocoque attachment shown in Fig. 7, involving four attachment fittings formed by termnations of longerons, avoids necessity of a separate tube subassembly for upper fitting. However, this may not be as satisfactory from a structural standpoint, as the material of the semi-monocoque section is not always as evenly loaded as with three-point attachment, and it would probably be necessary to use a slightly heavier gage sheet for the skin covering. To comprehend this factor, it should be understood that the semi-monocoque structure is rarely, if ever, a round section, but rather a sort of flattened elliptical section having a smaller minor axis at its upper end to meet the requirements of aerodynamic form, particularly with the smaller two-place tandem type of airplane wherein the fuselage must be deep and narrow. If the semi-monocoque structure could be designed as a true circular section, then the four point attachment would have definite structural advantages.

Tubing Alignment Clamp

I have found the illustrated clamp very useful in lining up tubing prior to welding, and it may be of interest to other builders. It is very simple to make, and allows adjustment for accuracy in the work being done.

The split-ring hangers and threaded rod can be pur-

chased at any plumbing supply store. The turnbuckle is readily available at any hardware store. Cut the threaded rod to the desired lengths, assemble the parts, and that's all there is to making it.

by Luckey J. Searcy

Split-Ring Pipe Hanger

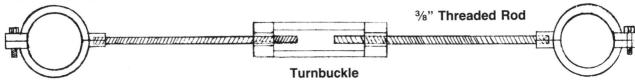

⅜" **Threaded Rod**

Turnbuckle

Welding Safely

by Jesse E. Goss, EAA 2751

Quite often aircraft homebuilders overlook welding procedures I consider to be very important — many are failing to oil the **inside** of the tubular assemblies **after welding.**

During the welding operation, the **inside** of the tubing is being heated also and the temperature is above that required to cause oxidation — burning of the metal. This oxidation will continue to eat away the metal at a dangerous rate. How to stop this oxidizing action and feel safer is the question.

First let me suggest an experiment — then we'll discuss the remedy. When you are ready to begin your welding operation secure a 6 in. piece of tubing approximately 1 in. O.D. Make up two washers from sheet stock of the same diameter as the tubing.

Note that the inside of the tubing is oily. Do not wash the tube. Weld one of the washers on one end of the tube. After welding this one end, use a good light and look into the open end of the tube. You can see the oxidation that has taken place. A scale has formed on the walls of the tubing. This scale formed because the underside of the heated metal has a strong affinity for the oxygen and nitrogen in the atmosphere.

Now proceed to complete the welding of the open end of the tube. Just as you are about to complete this weld, don't be surprised to see smoke and sometimes oil blow out from your weld. Perhaps you experienced a bit of difficulty in closing this "blow hole".

What happened? The heat from the welding torch caused the oil that was on the inside wall of the tubing to form a gas. The continued heat caused this gas to expand and "blow out" your molten metal. Convinced? That's the lesson — now to the remedy.

Drill two holes about 3/32 in. in diameter in your practice tube previously welded. Fill this tube with linseed oil — the oil doesn't need to be heated for our experiment. Now rotate the tube until the inside is covered with the oil. Drain all the oil from the tube. Saw the end from the tube about one in. from the end. Inspect the inside of the tube and note particularly how the oil has covered the "burned" or oxidized area of the weld.

The lesson we learn from this is that when a section of some tubular structure, such as a fuselage cross member or a diagonal brace, is inserted requiring welding at each end in such a manner that will seal the tube tightly closed, a vent hole is required to release the expanding gases. These holes are also needed in order to fill the tube with linseed oil so that the inside of the tube is treated in such a manner that the oxidation is stopped.

After cutting, fitting and checking the tubes to be welded, drill a small hole near the ends. These holes will serve as a vent for releasing the gases caused by the heat of the welding torch. Later these same holes can be used in filling each section of tubing with hot linseed oil. After filling with oil, the entire assembly should be rotated in such a manner that the inside of the tubes will be given a coat of oil. The oil should then be drained.

The placement of these holes is important. They should be so located that they will not interfere with installation of fairing strips or other fittings to be added later. These holes should be plugged with drive rivets. When you secure your drive rivets from the aviation supply house, be sure to check the size and drill the holes for a tight fit when the rivets are driven.

Now for some tips. After cutting the tubes to the proper length, wash inside and out with a cleaning solvent to remove the oil placed there by the manufacturer to prevent rust (oxidation). After filling the tubes with oil, you may use small wooden pegs in the vent holes to retain the oil while the assembly is being rotated.

The hot linseed oil can be inserted in any manner you may choose. A hand sump pump or a small rubber bulb that is commonly used in auto service stations to fill the car battery will come in handy.

An oxidizing flame is hotter than a slightly excess acetylene flame. Therefore the flame used when welding tubing of aircraft quality will have a slight excess of oxy- acetylene. This type of flame has a fluxing action and is called a reducing flame because it aids in reducing surface oxides. Yet this flame adjustment does not cause carbon pickup on the base metal. **Never** dig the

Because of space limitations, or unavailability of hangar space, many EAA'ers incorporate folding wings on their aircraft. They can then tow or trailer them home. Special fitting shown here was adapted for a high wing monoplane. These are critical welds and proper penetration, tolerances and strength are extremely important.

inner cone into the molten weld puddle as this will also cause oxidation.

On the thinner wall tubing and thin gussets it is preferable to use the scale welding method. This technique allows each weld puddle to cool slightly, thus giving the appearance of fish scales. Practice — **much practice** — is required to become proficient at welding chrome-molybdenum tubing. Practice pays off in a better weld.

The welding rod commonly used to weld aircraft tubing is a copper-coated, low-carbon draw iron. This rod contains a maximum of 0.06 carbon and also contains manganese and other elements. A rod of $\frac{1}{16}$ in. diameter will be sufficient for most of your welding. You could probably use a few pieces of $\frac{3}{32}$ in. rod on some of the larger fittings.

When you receive the rod from the welding supply house, note that it is slightly oily. Keep your rod wrapped and protected at all times. Just prior to use, remove a few pieces of the rod from the wrapping, and wipe clean before using. Never handle your clean rod with dirty, oily hands!

Do not grind, file or use emery cloth to smooth a weld. Use a wire brush for cleaning. Sand blasting prior to spray painting your prime coat is very good, but a little expensive. You may use a wire brush, but I prefer a soft bristle, stainless steel brush. After wire-brushing, clean with a good solvent just prior to prime.

This article concerns the hand welding of aircraft tubing when using the oxy-acetylene process. Heavier parts, such as landing gear fittings require heat treatment.

Although some persons do not consider welding a skilled craft, the homebuilder who masters welding can be proud, as welding is truly an art and a science. Weld 'em safely! Weld 'em good! Keep 'em flying!

Working With 4130 Tubing

Pipe Holder

1) To solve the problem of holding pipe for cutting, etc., I built a set of $\frac{1}{2}$" soft wood inserts to fit a 6" woodworking vise. One face of this wood was grooved out at a 45° saw cut angle on a radial saw set to the depth of about $\frac{1}{4}$". Two passes on the saw are necessary to produce each groove. As can be seen in Fig. 1, one horizontal, two vertical and two 45 degree angle grooves are cut into the face of one block. These grooves could be cut by hand using a medium coarse file if a power saw is not available. This rig holds pipe securely in any position with little tension on the vise and absolutely no danger of crushing the tube. The wooden blocks are held to the face of the vise by screws through the holes provided when the vise was manufactured. Mount vise on your work table to save steps. This vice works well with all normal and irregular shapes of wood, metal, fittings, etc. and can be utilized for any purpose after the plane is complete.

Tubing Grinder

2) A used washing machine motor, a stub mandrel and a 6" grinding wheel (medium coarse) was all it took to make a perfect grinder. I mounted this, plus a switch box, switch and steel cover plate on a piece of scrap $\frac{3}{4}$" plywood. The plywood is then clamped or bolted to the work table preferably behind the tubing vise. This little gem will save many hours of hand filing on a fuselage.

Work Table

3) When building your work table for the fuselage, make it about 2 feet longer than is required. This will allow space to mount the grinder, vise and an assortment of necessary tools. Construct table top so that it has an overhang of 1" to 2". This is used to C-clamp grinder, vise, etc. around perimeter of table.

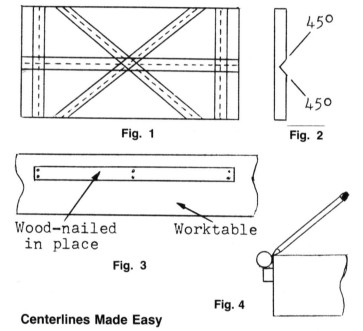

Fig. 1 **Fig. 2**

Wood-nailed in place   Worktable

Fig. 3

Fig. 4

Centerlines Made Easy

4) Obtain a fat bodied red or black marker containing permanent ink with a fine nylon point for marking centerlines on tubes. This works a lot better than the silver drafting pencil in common use. The silver pencil is still valuable for fine measurements such as marking location of rosette weld drill holes, etc.

5) Attach a scrap piece of lumber to the side of your work table or bench. I used a piece of $\frac{3}{4}$" plywood 2" wide and about 3' long. This was nailed in place $\frac{3}{8}$" below the top surface as shown in Fig. 3 to handle tube sizes from $\frac{1}{2}$" to $1\frac{1}{4}$". This is used to mark the centerline on tubes by placing the tube on this ledge and holding against the table as in the side view Fig. 4. Run the ink marker back and forth on the tube at the point where the tube touches the top of the table. Two or three strokes puts on a highly visable permanent centerline.

When welding, the drilling of a small hole (.063") as shown in the sketch does wonders for a person's work. This relieves gas pressure and prevents blow-holes, aids in the prevention of distortion, twisting, and bending. Also this helps during the circulation of preservative oil internally and vents the entire structure so condensation is retarded. A small amount of oil may remain trapped at cluster joints and this is where most scale and rust starts and the preservative is needed. As a reminder, keep the hole small so that not much metal is removed. A ⅟₁₆" drill is fine.

by Carl Anderson

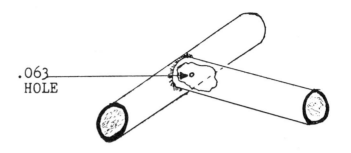

An Abrasive Cut-Off Saw

If you are contemplating building a steel-tube fuselage, you should have some method of quickly and easily cutting your tubing to the lengths required. The method I used while constructing the fuselage of my homebuilt was a home-made abrasive cut-off saw.

The construction is very simple. The machine is, in effect, a teeter-totter with a cut-off wheel at one end and a driving motor at the other. Construction is started with the frame which is made up of two by three-inch fir which is glued and screwed together to make a rigid framework. The frame must be square, as this squareness controls the squareness of the cut. The bearings used were self-aligning, and were mounted on the lower front end of the frame as shown. The drive motor is mounted on the top rear end of the frame, and its position will be determined by the length of the V belt used. Complete the frame by adding protective covers over the wheel and the belt.

Determine the balance point of the frame with everything mounted on it and move one inch forward and drill pivot holes through in line. This pivot hole must be square with the frame in all directions or a strain will be put on the wheel so that it may break, and the cuts made with the saw may not be square across the part cut.

A base is made as shown in the drawing, and the frame is mounted on it using a piece of tubing as a pivot. The frame should be mounted so that there is enough weight at the rear to keep the forward end up in the air. Locate the material-holding block on the center line of the wheel when it is tipped down. The block should be at 90 degrees to the face of the wheel.

The abrasive wheel can be purchased at any tool-supply house or at Sears or Montgomery Ward stores. The diameter of the wheel used on my saw was ten inches, but an eight-inch diameter will do as well as long as the center hole will fit the shaft used.

Provisions should be made to keep abrasive dust out of the motor, and the saw should be used away from other machinery as the dust flies quite a distance away from the machine. Also, be sure that material is held tightly in the cut-off block as it will break the wheel if it moves while it is being cut. The wheel should turn approximately 3500 rpm, so choose your pulleys to suit.

There are many variables possible in the size of the bearing used, the length of the shaft, and V belts available in constructing the machine, which would change almost all of any dimensions given, so put in your dimensions to suit the material at hand. You will be surprised at how well your abrasive saw will work on metals.

by W.L. 'Bill' Dean

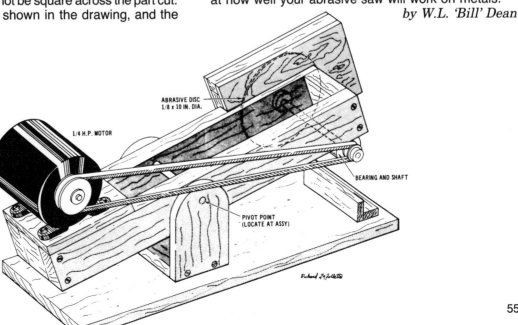

Fuselage Construction

The first order of business in the construction of a steel tube fuselage begins with the plans at the drawing board. Following construction of a flat level table, (at a comfortable working level), the tubing center line dimensions for the side of the fuselage are transferred from the plans to full size on the table top. Be very conscientious in all measurements for accuracy is extremely important. A mistake at this stage can have serious consequences later. Small blocks are then nailed so that tubing can be fitted and held into position while the various pieces are cut, filed and fitted into position for tack welding.

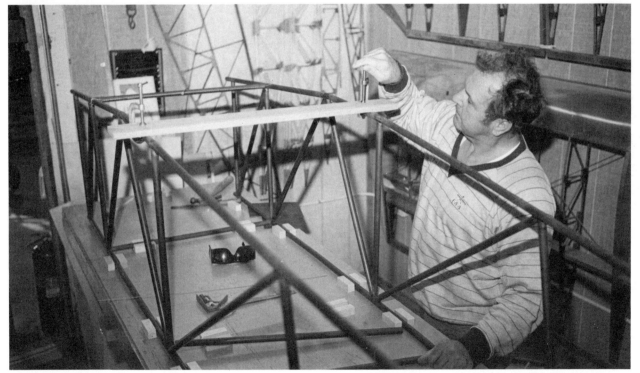

After both fuselage sides have been tack welded the top fuselage dimensions are transferred to the table top, wooden blocks nailed accordingly, and the two sides are mounted into position. Cross members can then be fitted and tack welded to both bottom and top to form the basic fuselage box. Use clamps to hold structure when fitting and welding, as shown above. Accuracy at each stage in building the fuselage box is absolutely vital. Use a plumb line and square to constantly check alignment so that everything turns out true to dimensions called for in the plans. With the tack welded fuselage box removed from the jib, Paul Poberezny, left, expertly welds all the tubing on his newly designed and modernized Corben Super Ace fuselage.

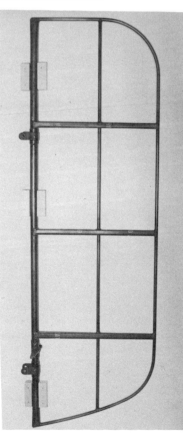

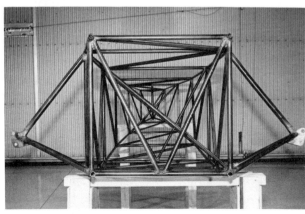

58

The Modernized Corben Super Ace

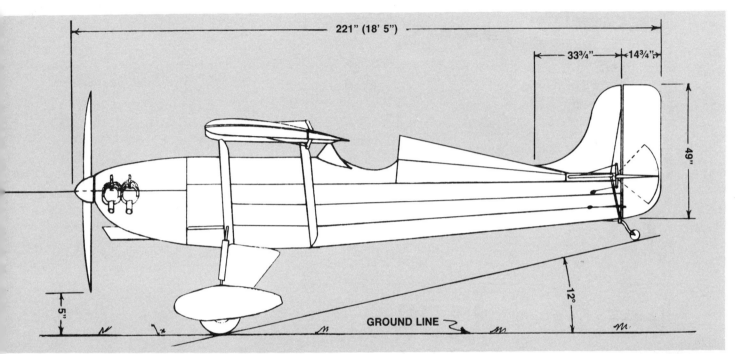

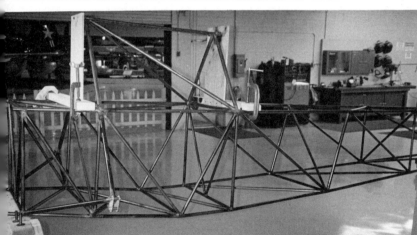

Starting from the front, welding of all joints is accomplished bay by bay in a circular route to the rear of the fuselage. At all times the welder must check to maintain accuracy of alignment and eliminate any distortion that may occur. Jigs are constructed for control surfaces, engine mount, cabane struts and landing gear assemblies to hold tubing in place for welding. Left shows how two rods are used to locate the square tubes that will receive the wing bolts at the top of the cabane. Note clamped plywood jibs used to align the rods accurately. After welding, control surfaces usually require no further work and can be covered, as the Corben fin shown above illustrates. Poberezny's modernized Super Ace will look similar to the drawing above — an attractive sport plane any builder would be proud to own and fly.

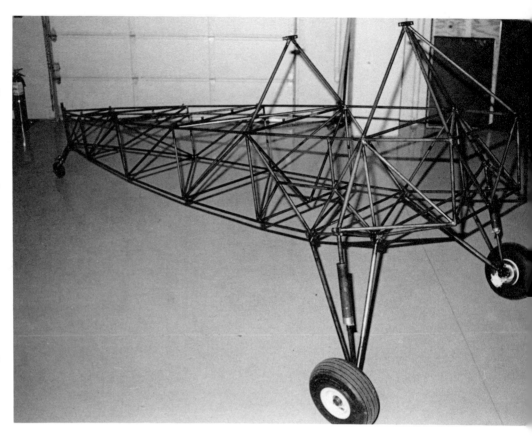

It is generally conceded that a steel tube fuselage provides the most crashworthy structure — as the tubing can absorb more "g's" as it collapses around the pilot. Aluminum is second in crashworthiness, with composite and wood structure third — the latter tending to shatter on impact. This is one reason why Paul Poberezny has retained the steel tube fuselage on all his designs. Fuselage (right) is Paul's modernized Corben Junior Ace as it sits 'on-the-gear'. This two place side-by-side parasol is a design that originated in the 1930s by C.C. 'Ace' Corben of Madison, Wis. He introduced a series of sharp looking, good performing sport planes for the homebuilders of that era.

Welding 4130 Chromium-Molybdenum Steel Tubing

Welding is undoubtedly the most important means by which tubing is joined, in the building of homebuilt aircraft.

In fabricating 4130 tubing into aircraft structures, oxy-acetylene welding is widely used and is the only welding method used on complicated joints in light-gauge materials.

Design

Oxy-cetylene welding is fundamentally simple. The edges of two pieces of metal are brought close together, heated to a molten state by means of the oxy-acetylene flame and after an intermingling of the molten metal allowed to cool down. Upon reaching room temperature there is but one piece of metal with, in effect, no joint at all. In practical application, of course, it is not as simple as that, but this fundamental simplicity does make it possible to produce excellent results with proper design and welding technique.

The Two Divisions of Joint Design: In welding the subject of joint design is usually considered as consisting of two parts. The first and simpler is the design of the weld cross section. The second is the design of the joint between two or more parts.

Weld Cross Section

Edge Preparation: With material less than 1/8" thick no special preparation is necessary except to make sure a good fit is obtained and that edges are cleaned of scale, grease and other dirt. For material 1/8" thick and heavier, the edges to be welded together should be beveled to provide an angle for a firm fit.

Spacing: Most welds in aircraft work are fillet welds of one form or another and for this type of weld no spacing is needed. For butt-type welds the edges to be joined should be spaced somewhat to facilitate thorough penetration. This spacing at the point of welding should be at least 1/32" for the lighter gauges to 1/8"

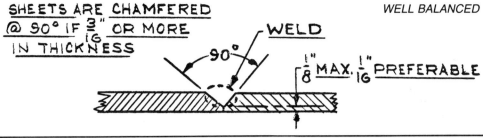

SHEETS ARE CHAMFERED @ 90° IF $\frac{3}{16}$" OR MORE IN THICKNESS

90°

WELD

$\frac{1}{8}$" MAX. $\frac{1}{16}$" PREFERABLE

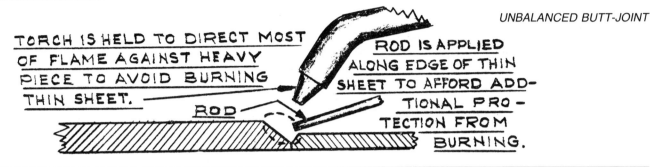

TORCH IS HELD TO DIRECT MOST OF FLAME AGAINST HEAVY PIECE TO AVOID BURNING THIN SHEET.

ROD IS APPLIED ALONG EDGE OF THIN SHEET TO AFFORD ADDITIONAL PROTECTION FROM BURNING.

ROD

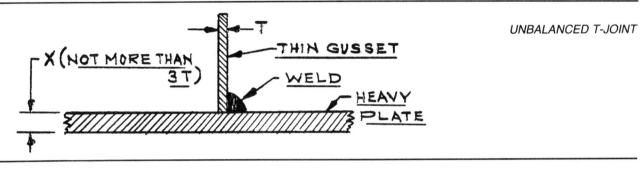

X (NOT MORE THAN 3T)

THIN GUSSET

WELD

HEAVY PLATE

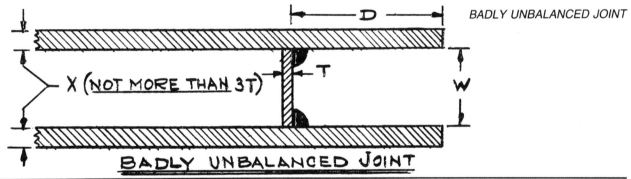

D

T

W

X (NOT MORE THAN 3T)

BADLY UNBALANCED JOINT

for plate material.

Weld Penetration: Thorough fusion between the base metal and metal added from the welding rod at all points in the weld is a necessary requirement of all fusion welding.

Weld Reinforcement: By reinforcement is meant the amount by which the weld is built up above the top surfaces of the parts being joined. Such reinforcement should merge smoothly into the top surfaces without undercutting or excessive buildup at any point. Fur butt welds in 4130 sheet or tubing welded with low-carbon or medium-carbon welding rod, the weld should be built up so as to be about 1¼ times the base-metal thickness.

Welding Rod: Curiously enough, better results are frequently obtained in the oxy-acetylene welding of low-alloy steels when the welding rod has an analysis which is different from that of the base metal. For 4130 this takes the directions of a lower alloy content in the rod. With thin sections which are not to be subsequently heat-treated, a rod with the analysis 0.06% carbon max., 0.25% manganese max., and not over 0.05% silicon has been used a great deal with completely satisfactory results. For parts which are subsequently to be heat-treated or in which somewhat higher strengths are desired in the weld, a welding rod somewhat higher in carbon is recommended. A rod having 0.14 to 0.18% carbon, approximately 1.10% manganese and 0.37% silicon has found wide acceptance for some time and its use seems to be expanding. The manganese and silicon in this rod have a fluxing action which is advantageous.

Welding Technique: This subject is abstracted here and more completely discussed in other articles. A slightly excess acetylene flame adjustment is recommended for welding with either of the welding rods mentioned and 4130 base metal. One important reason for this is that the slight amount of carbon in the flame has a fluxing action which is of considerable aid in reducing surface oxides; yet such a flame adjustment does not cause carbon pick-up by the base metal.

A purely theoretical analysis of the metallurgy of the base metal and of the welding action may indicate a neutral flame as desirable. However, the presence of surface oxide and the fact that the flame adjustment may fluctuate slightly strengthen the argument in favor of a slight excess acetylene feather in the flame.

Design of Joinings Between Structural Parts

The design of the joinings between two or more pieces of tubing is dictated in most cases by the final structure desired. There are certain basic designs, of course, such as those between two pieces of tubing whose axis are to be in the same straight line or, in another case, perpendicular to each other.

Effect of Welding Heat On 4130

Most tubing used in aircraft is purchased in the normalized condition or, in other words, it has been heated to a temperature above the critical, soaked there a sufficiently long time to be certain the metal has reached a uniform temperature throughout, and then allowed to cool to room temperature in still air. Since 4130 is an air-hardening steel, such normalized tubing possesses higher strength and hardness and slightly lower ductility than if it had been cooled slowly in a furnace.

During welding the edges to be joined are heated to a molten condition and allowed to cool in air. Because of the nature of the welding operation, in a relatively narrow zone adjacent to the weld there will be metal which was heated (1) considerably above the critical, (2) just above the critical, (3) not quite up to the critical, and (4) only slightly heated. After welding the hot metal will cool down more rapidly than if the whole tube was heated, since nearby cool metal will have a quenching effect. That gives three important effects to be considered, namely, expansion and contraction, air-hardening, and annealing.

Expansion and Contraction: Of course, when a weld area is heated, the metal expands, and upon cooling, contracts. Out of this come two factors of importance to the designer as well as the welding operator - distortion and locked-up stresses - and a third factor which is a property of the particular steel being considered - "white-shortness."

Distortion: The elimination of distortion is largely a function of the welding shop but the builder must consider it in order to decide how completely he can expect it to be eliminated. During the years that aircraft tubing has been welded, the welding shops have become particularly clever in eliminating distortion. The amount of shrinkage to be expected has been estimated and

proper allowances made. The builder must realize, however, that the amount of angular distortion and the amount of lateral distortion which result from the last weld in a closed structure vary with the amount of heat the welding operator uses, and there is, therefore, a limit to the closeness of the tolerances to be expected. An instance which illustrates a design calling for too small a tolerance concerns the fabrication of a motor mount on which it was expected also to support a small oil tank. The welding shop was able to hold the face-to-face dimensions of the mount to extremely close tolerance. Fixed brackets for the mounting of the oil tank added the requirement of keeping accurate angular alignment and straightness of the motor mount ring supporting tubes, and this caused considerable difficulty in the welding shop. A slight redesign to provide a small adjustment in the bracket would have met the condition with far less effort and better final results.

Locked-Up Stresses: There are two sources of locked-up stresses. When cold-work, such as bending or flattening, is performed on tubing, stresses are locked up in the metal. Practically all stresses caused by the manufacture of the tubing are relieved by the normalizing treatment.

During the contraction which follows welding, rather high stresses are locked up in the metal which was heated. However, in static tension, compression, or torsion, these stresses do not cause any particular difficulty (provided there has not been any serious impairment of ductility) unless there is but little unstressed material adjacent to the weld. When a part is loaded, the internal stresses induced seem to continue to move about until all the metal which is available to carry the load has been stressed to its yield point. Then permanent deformation begins.

For the builder this means that he should avoid placing welds too closely together. For instance, a short tube welded at both ends into a rigid structure cannot absorb a great deal of additional stress (in the same direction as those induced by welding). It becomes necessary for the builder to consider therefore, where stresses induced by cold work or by welding will be located, so that they may be distributed as uniformly as possible throughout the structure. Frequently it will be found advisable to remove the effects of cold work on bent and formed tubes by renormalizing or annealing before welding.

by Stan Dzik

Simplified Method of Fitting Aircraft Tubing

For anyone who has access to a lathe, here is an exceptionally simple and inexpensive method of fitting aircraft tubing. We used this method of fitting the tubing on our homebuilt, and we had the fuselage completed and on the gear in less than 100 hours.

The tubing is held in a block that is mounted on the cross-feed head of the lathe, a reamer is chucked in the lathe head, and the tubing is oriented so that the reamer cut results in an almost perfect fitting member. This method is not only quicker than most other methods, but it also results in stronger welded joints.

The fitting device can be made from a 4 in. by 4 in. piece of hardwood and several bolts for almost no cost. We made a block to fit each size of tubing, and it usually took about 15 minutes to make each block. We tried making one large diameter block and using sleeves to make it fit the smaller tubing, but this was not satisfactory.

To construct the block, we found that the best way to do it was to cut the block to size and drill the hole for the ½ in. hold-down bolt. Next mount the block on the cross-feed head and locate the center of the tubing hole. Mark the center lines of the hole on the end face of the block so that they can be used as reference lines during the cutting process. Now drill the tubing hole, saw the slot into the tubing hole and install the tubing lock bolt and nut.

A straight reference line is now drawn on the side of the piece of tubing that is being fitted, and the angle between the member to be fitted and an adjacent member is measured with a protractor. The tubing is placed in the block and the reference line on the tubing is aligned with one of the reference marks on the block. Next the cross-feed head is loosened and the measured angle is set up between the piece of tubing and the reamer. The cross-feed head is locked and the tubing is ready to cut. Feed the tubing into the reamer slowly while applying cutting oil. When the first end is cut to the proper depth, measure the angle between the members at the other end and reverse ends of the tubing in the block. Align the reference line on the tubing with the correct reference mark on the block so that the finished cuts will be oriented properly with respect to one another. Now set the tubing at the proper angle and repeat the cutting process until the member is of the correct length.

A little practice on some scrap pieces of tubing will give the operator enough experience to start fitting the tubing on his plane. This method was a great time saver for us and I hope it will benefit other members in their work.

by Michael Smith

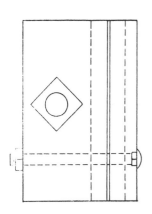 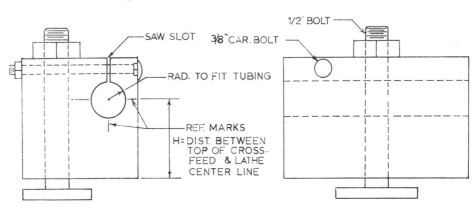

SAW SLOT   3/8" CAR. BOLT   1/2" BOLT

RAD. TO FIT TUBING

REF. MARKS
H=DIST. BETWEEN TOP OF CROSS-FEED & LATHE CENTER LINE

Random Notes on Welded Steel Tube Structures

by Antoni (Tony) Bingelis

The problems we most frequently encounter in building steel tube fuselages, or for that matter most welded components, are those resulting from the welding process itself.

Here's what happens everytime you weld a tubular joint.

As the tubing is heated, tremendous pressure is exerted in the area of the weld by the expanding hot metal; at the same time just a bit further away, the metal is cooler and unyielding. It resists the expansion. As a result, as soon as the heated area becomes plastic (molten), it succumbs to the resisting pressures around it and the molten area compresses and thickens in the process. This relieves the pressure in the expanding weld area.

When the weld is completed the heat of the torch is withdrawn and the metal starts to cool. Contraction takes place as the joint area tries to return to its original shape and dimension. But because the weld area was compressed during its molten state by the surrounding cooler metal, and because the metal now is no longer molten, the tubing will contract beyond its original configuration in making up for the diminished metal area caused by the original thickening that took place during welding. The resultant contraction is shown in figure 1.

Let's Get It Straight

It seems to be a common belief that if you normalize a weld the tube will relieve itself of both the internal stress and the distortion. This is not so. Although the internal stress will be relieved, the distortion will not be. The distortion, if allowed to remain uncorrected, can endow your airplane with a bad case of the uglies or cause other difficulties depending on the locations where they take place.

For instance, you may have noticed after completing the fuselage welds that the longerons are bowed-in between some stations. This little cosmetic problem can be corrected by playing the torch flame along the outside portion of the longeron. Get the tube red hot and the longeron will probably return to its proper straight alignment. But what if it doesn't? In that case, the friendly persuasion of a rubber mallet may be exercised. For slight bends a rubber mallet's gentle influence (on the cold tubing) should be sufficient. Take care, however, not to dent or damage the tubing!

Try to remember that anytime you heat metal, it will increase in dimension . . . both in length and in breadth. Conversely, as it cools, it will contract but, because of the process described earlier, welded areas tend to contract a little more than they expanded.

Once you realize that the expansion/contraction process can no more be eliminated than the resulting localized shrinkage, you will learn to allow for it.

Fuselage Assembly Practices

The accepted assembly practice is to tack-weld a fuselage together before undertaking the completion of the welds at each tube cluster. This permits you to at least begin with a good alignment of everything. Nevertheless, continuously check the alignment during and after welding each bay, to determine what effect, if any, has been transmitted to other tack-welded areas.

I'm sure that one of the first lessons learned regarding fuselage assembly is the discovery that it is virtually impossible to insert diagonal tubes in place once the fuselage cross members are fitted and tacked. The obvious procedure is to fit and position the diagonals at each bay before installing the cross members in the next bay.

Incidentally, if you intend to treat the fuselage interior with a rust preventative treatment — don't forget to drill ⅛" holes in the longerons at every point of intersection with an upright tube, cross member, or a diagonal. The idea is to interconnect the entire structure with a passageway for the introduction of a rust preventative fluid. More on this later.

The Welding Sequence

Always start to finish-weld a tacked fuselage at the firewall and work toward the tail end, a single bay at a time. Complete welding each cluster before moving to the next bay. This method should minimize the amount of distortion and misalignment resulting from the welding process.

I would advise against installing and attempting to align any fittings until **after** the basic tubular structure has been completed. Accuracy in the alignment of components such as landing gear lugs, wing attachment fittings and the tail attachment fittings is then possible.

Try The Sub-Assembly Method

One way to reduce the undesireable effects of contraction resulting from the welding is to pre-fabricate portions of the structure as subassemblies.

Certain tube clusters are very difficult to reach when an attempt is made to assemble them along with the main structure. Trying to finish-weld clusters in confined areas can be frustrating. It may be better, therefore, to jig such assemblies on a workbench or in some

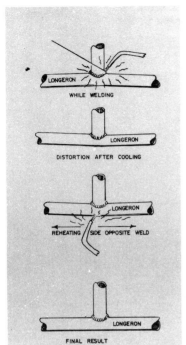

Fig. 1

Effect Of Heating
And Cooling
On Longerons

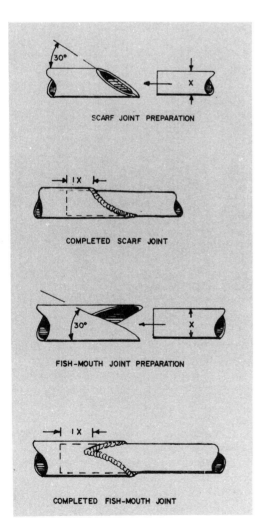

Fig. 2   Joints For Reducing
Longeron Size

other convenient welding location to finish-weld, straighten and normalize the subassembly beforehand. Then when you do install it in the primary structure the only welds remaining to be made are the legends attaching it to the main frame. Some landing gear trusses fall in this category.

About Splicing Longerons

Sometimes longerons must be spliced because the designer calls out a tubing size reduction in the longerons just aft of the cockpit. Designers often do this because loads and stresses are lower nearer the tail.

To effect the dimensional reduction in the longerons called for, use either scarf joints or fish-mouth joints. These joints will, when properly made and welded, result in greater strength than the original tubing. The angle of cut for either type of joint is made at 30 degrees to the centerline of the tube. For my part, I think the fish-mouth splice is the better joint for longerons.

I would highly recommend that you make the splice and complete the welding of each as a subassembly before inserting the longerons in the fuselage assembly jig. This assembly technique should outwit the "shrink gremlins" and allow you to maintain dimensional accuracy in the fuselage.

In making these longeron splices a smaller diameter tubing is telescoped into the larger a short distance, approximately equal to the diameter of the smaller tube. Someone is sure to ask how good a fit is needed for this splice. Well, in making a fish-mouth splice, the fit between the smaller and larger tube may be somewhat on the loose side. However, for the scarf-joint type of splice, the fit between the telescoped tubes must be fairly close. Use the next size smaller tube and it will be just about right.

Controlling Warpage

To attach tail surface hinges, a fairly heavy weld must be made along the centerline of the stabilizer spar and likewise on the facing side of the elevator torque tube spar. Each of these tubes will warp due to the welding shrinkage at the point of each hinge weldment.

So, weld those hinges first . . . finish them before inserting the tube into the tail assembly jig. By prefabricating the tail spar tubes separately they can be straightened easily by applying heat to the side opposite from the welded hinge.

I guess the general rule, if there is one, is to look at each assembly and determine if it might best be welded up as a sub-unit.

Similarly, an engine mount requires the maintenance of accurate alignment throughout the welding process because, as the tubing is heated and welded, it "walks around" quite a bit. It is not unusual to complete welding an engine mount only to find that the mounting bolt holes are misaligned . . . sometimes by as much as ⅜". Rigid jigging, therefore, is a must for engine mount construction.

The basic alignment problem, I find, occurs because some builders will not take time to build a rigid

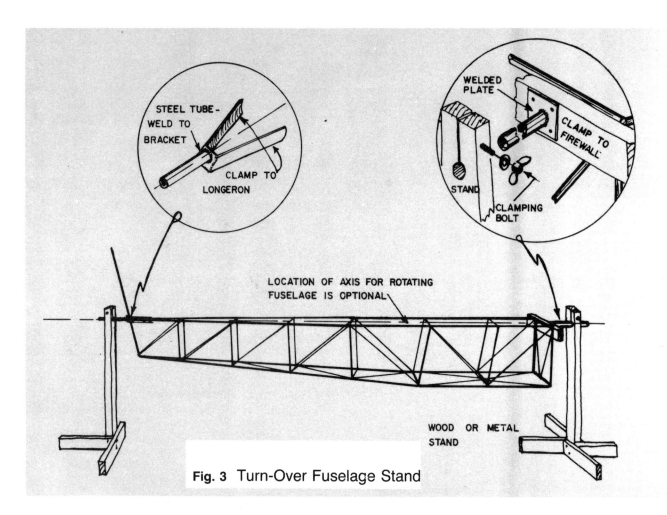

STEEL TUBE-
WELD TO
BRACKET

CLAMP TO
LONGERON

WELDED
PLATE

CLAMP TO
FIREWALL

STAND

CLAMPING
BOLT

LOCATION OF AXIS FOR ROTATING
FUSELAGE IS OPTIONAL

WOOD OR METAL
STAND

Fig. 3 Turn-Over Fuselage Stand

metal jig. Instead, they use wood and plywood. Both will char and burn during welding. The charring usually causes the bolt holes to become oversized or elongated . . . and that is when problems and errors multiply.

Most all-wood European designs feature engine mounts welded to rather large metal plates (fittings) which serve as attachment points for bolting the mount to the firewall. The large steel fittings do an excellent job of distributing localized loads in a wood structure but they are difficult, very difficult to weld to thin-wall engine mount tubes. You learn this quickly because by the time you get the steel plate to a molten state, the thin wall of the tubing has been overheated and has started to disappear before your eyes. And, try as you may, it is difficult to lay a good bead without burning away the tubing.

Then later (assuming you were fairly successful), when you turn the mount over for welding the flip-side, the challenge becomes just too much because then you have the just completed weld on the reverse side contributing a temperature-robbing-mass to your problem of getting enough welding heat in the right place. What to do? Well, it would be nice to have somebody heliarc weld the mount, of course. However, your best course of action is to arrange to have someone play another torch over the metal fitting to preheat it and to keep its temperature up while you concentrate on making a good weld. It is the differential in the heat required that causes you to burn through the thin wall tubing. Alternatively, you might switch to a heavier wall tubing.

Welding .049" tubing is much less demanding than using .035" wall thickness. Even easier to weld would be tubing having a wall thickness of .065" but here we go with a significant increase in weight. At any rate, remember that preheating the heavier metal areas and keeping them up to red heat will afford you the best chance for making successful welds in this kind of a welding situation.

A Turn-Over Fuselage Stand Is A Must

You don't have to have a bum back or a trick knee to appreciate the usefulness of a rotating stand. Think of the convenience of having your fuselage supported at just the right height and providing free access to all parts of the structure. But best of all, a turn-over stand can be a real back saver and a tireless silent servant to your needs. It will hold the fuselage structure steady for you in an infinite number of positions. It will enable you to gain easier access to hard-to-get-to areas of the fuselage and it will allow you to do a better job of welding.

You can make one of your own from odds and ends commonly found around the house and shop. Furthermore, it can be as simple or as complex as you care to make it . . . and, it doesn't have to take 9 G's either! In essence, all you need is a simple support for each end of the fuselage frame which will permit it to be rotated as if it were between centers in a lathe.

At one end, the firewall-end preferably, a provision will be needed for locking or clamping the fuselage

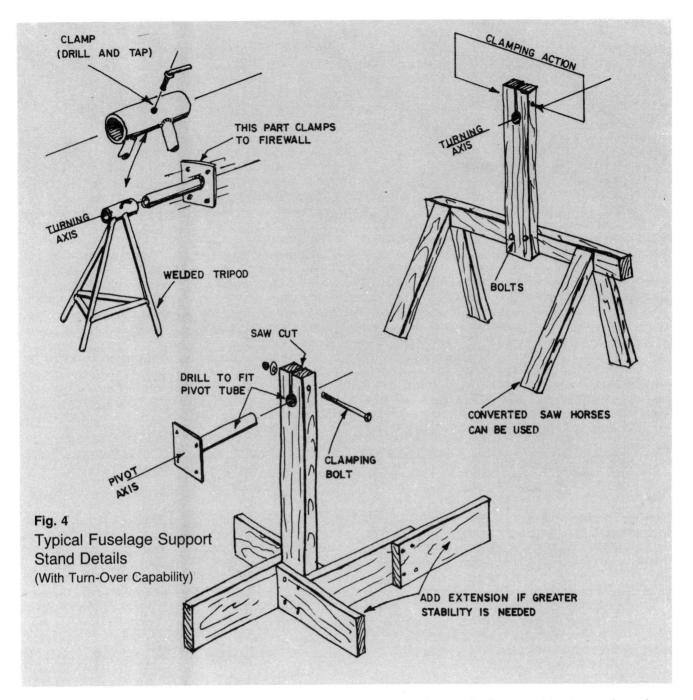

CLAMP
(DRILL AND TAP)

THIS PART CLAMPS
TO FIREWALL

TURNING
AXIS

WELDED TRIPOD

CLAMPING ACTION

TURNING
AXIS

BOLTS

CONVERTED SAW HORSES
CAN BE USED

SAW CUT

DRILL TO FIT
PIVOT TUBE

CLAMPING
BOLT

PIVOT
AXIS

Fig. 4
Typical Fuselage Support
Stand Details
(With Turn-Over Capability)

ADD EXTENSION IF GREATER
STABILITY IS NEEDED

against rotating after it has been turned to the position you want. Sketches of a few details for such a device are shown in Figures 3 and 4.

These stands work! They are easy to make since they do not have to support much more than 50 pounds on either end. I recommend the use of such a stand very highly. After all the welding is completed, use the stand later during the fabric covering process too. Similar rigs have saved a number of my friends no end of hardship and, in one instance in particular, even made the welding job possible.

About That Rust Prevention Treatment

After the welding is completed you have to decide whether or not internal oiling (rust prevention treatment) is necessary.

Some old-timers will tell you they have never found an internally rusted tube except in cases where there was a hole or crack or some form of ventilation in the structure that could have allowed internal condensation to collect.

Others will say they've replaced many a tube, especially in the tail end of tail draggers . . . so, decide for yourself.

Tubing, as received from the supplier, will have some sort of a dried film inside to protect it from internal corrosion. But as soon as you do any welding on the tubing this protective film burns off and an oxide forms. In time, corrosion appears and spreads throughout. It becomes important, therefore, to provide a new protective film to cover the inside of the completed structure. However, there is no use coating the inside of the tubing with a rust preventative film until **after** all of the welding has been completed as each time another weld is made, the process burns away the rust inhibiting film

67

around the weld.

A good rust inhibitor is plain ol' linseed oil. Boiled linseed oil is the stuff builders and mechanics have been using since the advent of welded structures.

The rust preventative treatment requires the entire fuselage (or any other tubular structure) to be filled and sloshed thoroughly with hot linseed oil. After that chore is completed the excess linseed oil is drained and the openings sealed. Here's one way to do it.

Heat the linseed oil to approximately 200°F to make it flow better. Obtain a metal container with an outlet in the bottom. Fill it with linseed oil and hang it up high, or position it on a bench or shelf so that it will be higher than the structure being treated. This lets gravity flow to do your work.

For example, to treat a fuselage tilt it so that the tail end is low and introduce the linseed oil through the open end(s) of the longeron(s) at the firewall. Keep adding the oil to the structure until the gurgling in the lower end subsides or you think you have added enough to fill most of the structure. This is another job you can't hurry.

Remove the hose and then close the opening(s) by welding a small steel disc across the open end of each longeron. Since the fuselage is tilted, the oil will have flowed to the lowered aft end away from the welding heat. Be sure to clean the weld area of the rust pre-ventative oil before making the welds (cough, cough, smoke you know).

After everything has cooled off enough to permit handling, rotate the fuselage this way and that and turn it end-for-end at least once. Allow the fuselage to remain in various attitudes long enough for the oil to seep into all the uprights, diagonals and nooks and crannies (nooks and crannies??). When you are convinced that the structure is totally oil coated internally, drill a small hole (about 3/32" dia.) in the aft end of each longeron and drain out the excess oil. Try to recapture it in a container . . . even so, it will be almost as messy a process as draining it on the ground. Still, draining it into a container will give you some measure that you have drained most of it out. If you get more drained linseed oil than you put in, you might consider going into the oil business . . . you could make a mint! The last step is to plug all external drain holes and the openings into which the oil was introduced if you haven't already done so. Use small self-tapping screws to plug the drilled drain holes.

Allow the fuselage to set a day or so in the tail low attitude and then remove the drain screws at the tail end once again. Allow whatever oil that has accumulated to drain until it quits running. Don't forget to replace the hole plugs (screws).

Now, that wasn't so hard, was it?

Tips for Cutting Tubing

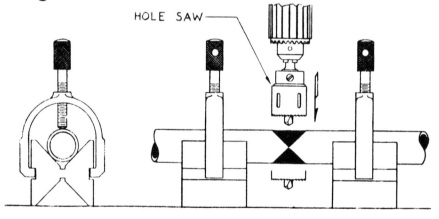

Most mechanics resort to the time-honored method of hacksawing and filing when fitting the ends of steel tubing together for welding. The amateur aircraft builder, however, finds this to be tedious when cutting the many tubes in a fuselage. One of the simpler ways of doing it faster is to get a dressing tool and shape the face of a grinding wheel into semi-circular form. However, I have found that there is yet another simple, inexpensive trick, particularly helpful when many tubes have to be fitted.

Purchase a standard hole cutting saw the same size as the tubing. These saws are available at all good hardware stores. Put it into a drill press set for high speed, place the tubing to be cut on the drill table with any suitable vee-block and clamp arrangement, making sure the tube is held so that it cannot turn in any direction, and just bring the saw down. These saws will cut over their own diameter in depth and as a result the tube will be severed completely in one pass. The end shape which results is perfect for a 90° joint. I have found this scheme works best on right angle cutoffs, but you can experiment on other cuts if you wish. The "U" cuts made in this way can quickly be deepened with a round-faced grinding wheel or even a rat tail file when 45 deg. joints are needed.

by Bruce E. Graham, EAA 4303

Welding Tips

Although 4130 steel (chrome molybdenum or "chrome-moly") is very tough and strong when cold, it is even weaker than mild steel in the heated condition; therefore, it must not be stressed or shocked while in a white-hot state. The following guidelines should be heeded if problems are to be avoided:

1. Do your welding in a draft-free area, otherwise the metal will chill too fast and thereby be weakened.
2. Never use tightly clamped jigs. Spring-type clamps are just fine for holding parts to be welded, and they come in various sizes.
3. Good welders say that starting welding on an edge is not a good technique. Rather, it is best to start at a point away from the edge and work to it. **Caution** — heat builds up fast near the easily heated edges and it is very, very easy to inadvertently burn through the edge of the metal. Watch it and draw the flame away slightly as needed when the edge itself is reached. If you do ruin a piece, make it over. That's where the educational part of homebuilding comes in.
4. In all cases where parts have been tack-welded together, it is most important that you melt completely through the tack as you complete the final weld.
5. As the thickness of the metal being welded decreases, the selection of the proper tip and the adjustment of the gases becomes very important. Thin metals are easily buckled when too much heat is used.
6. Especially on thin metal and thin-wall tubing, care needs to be taken to clean any dirt, scale, or oxide from the parts to be welded. Percentagewise, as the parent metal becomes thinner, the chances of having dirty metal in the weld is increased. Take time to clean the weld areas.
7. Get in the habit of preheating the metal in the area to be welded.
8. Don't clamp your work in the vise and then try to weld on the part near the jaws of the vise as the heavy metal of the vise will draw away the heat and you'll have difficulty getting the metal hot enough to do good work. Remember, any large or heavy metal areas near the weld areas of work will draw away the heat from the joint and will require a larger flame, thereby increasing the risk of burning the adjacent metal.
9. Be sure your line of weld in the parent metal is heated to proper melting point. Try to keep the weld pool size as uniform as possible.
10. Heat the filler rod to the same melting point before introducing it into the melted pool of metal.
11. Add filler rod as evenly and steadily as possible.
12. Don't rush! Be sure that the added metal and parent metal are puddled together properly.
13. Keep playing the outer envelope flame over the pool to protect it from the oxidizing effect of the air.
14. Melt a certain portion of the parent metal on both sides for the entire length of the weld.
15. Avoid reheating of weld metal which has cooled.

by Tony Bingelis

Making Hard-to-Guess Tube Angles for Cutting

Those who have tried to cut and fit tubing know that it is a tedious trial and error exercise at best.

A clever solution to this problem in simple terms, is a length of elastic which is sewn over a backing material length-wise every ⅛". Wires or small welding rod is inserted between each sewn strip. After all the wires are inserted into the elastic, it is wrapped around a piece of the tubing to be fitted. Use a rubber band to hold the marking device together.

The next step is to push this item up so that the individual wires contact the structure to be fitted. After all the wires are pushed into contact, slide the whole marking gadget back. Draw a pencil line around the contour formed by the wire tips. Use a silver pencil so that the line can be seen.

Cut and file the end down to the line. The fit will please you.

by Ralph King

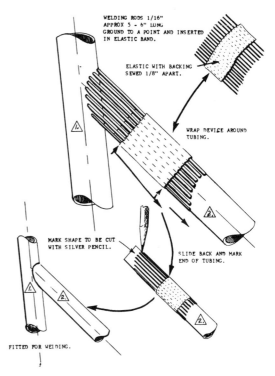

WELDING RODS 1/16" APPROX 5 - 6" LONG, GROUND TO A POINT AND INSERTED IN ELASTIC BAND.

ELASTIC WITH BACKING SEWED 1/8" APART.

WRAP DEVICE AROUND TUBING.

MARK SHAPE TO BE CUT WITH SILVER PENCIL.

SLIDE BACK AND MARK END OF TUBING.

FITTED FOR WELDING.

Structural Tubing Repair

Repair Of Structural Steel Tubing

a. General. Repairs to structural tubes consist of smoothing small nicks, scratches, and dents, reinforcing cracked members, reinforcing dented areas, splicing damaged members, replacing damaged members when splicing is impractical, and correcting minor distortion. With the exception of correcting minor distortion, all repairs are accomplished by welding. Electric arc welding and oxyacetylene welding are acceptable, and the welding method used will be determined by the location of the damage and the available equipment. The nature of damage will determine whether or not a fuselage section must be removed from the fuselage truss. In general, smoothing small dents and correcting minor distortion can usually be accomplished without disassembly of the major components. The intense heat caused by all types of welding necessitates isolating the area to be welded from all parts or members which might be injured by contact with heat. Heavy wet rags will provide sufficient insulation to prevent heat distortion or damage to adjacent parts. All fire precautions should be observed before any welding is started. Structural tubing or structural sheet stock used for the repair of structural steel tubes is of 1025, X 4130, or NE8630 (National Emergency) steel. Tubing used for telescope reinforcements or for splicing must be of at least the same tensile strength and wall thickness as that of the original member. Zinc chromate primer used throughout this section shall be of Specification No. AN-TT-P-656.

b. Negligible damage to steel tubing. Some forms of damage to tubular structures may be considered negligible. Such damage may take the form of slight indentations, scratches or minor bowing. Smooth dents not exceeding 1/20 of the tube diameter in depth, without cracks, fractures, or sharp corners, and clear of the middle third of the length of the member may be disregarded except to satisfy appearance. Tubular members should be carefully examined for the presence of sharp nicks and deep scratches. These nicks and scratches produce stress concentrations that may cause failure of the part. Care must be taken to smooth out all sharp nicks and deep scratches with a fine file, fine emery paper or steel wool. When this is accomplished, high concentrations of stress disappear.

Repair Of Fuselage Tubing

a. Welding of steel - general. The process of joining steel parts by welding consists in fusing the metal of the welding wire or rod with the metal of the joint ends until the joint is built up with new metal. This process can be accomplished by either electric arc welding or by oxyacetylene welding. The fused metal of the joint is of a cast structure and does not have the physical properties or strength of the metal parts or the welding wire before being fused. The section of the tube adjoining a gas weld will be annealed by the welding heat for a distance of from ¼ to ¾ inch on each side of the weld. In cases of electric arc welding, this distance will be greatly reduced, as the weld proceeds much faster than in the case of gas welding and no preheating of the material is necessary. The melting point of steel is approximately 1193 to 1493° C (2180 to 2720° F). A combination eye and face shield and a leather apron should be worn while welding and proper ventilation should be provided. Inasmuch as the presence of gas vapors will be a fire hazard, all necessary fire precautions must be taken before any welding is attempted. Use sandpaper or wire brush to clean all affected areas prior to welding if a completely new weld is to be made. If a weld is to be made over a failure in an electric weld bead, chip and file off all the existing bead before applying a new weld to the area.

CAUTION: After a weld is made, do not file or smooth the weld or apply any solder or other filler to improve the appearance of the weld.

---

b. Electric arc welding of steel. Before starting to weld, make certain that the surface of the parts to be welded is free of loose scales, oxides, oil and foreign matter; dip all replacement tubes and inner reinforcing sleeves into hot 74° C (156° F) raw linseed oil, then wipe oil from outer circumference of the tubes. This treatment protects the interior of the tubes from corrosion. Outer reinforcing sleeves do not require this treatment. Jigs, clamping devices and tack welding shall be used wherever required to control warping and insure proper alignment. Preheating is usually required only on heavy fittings and forgings, and chamfering is usually required only on material of 0.140 inch wall thickness and greater. The proper electric arc welding rods to be used with chrome molybdenum steel shall be in accordance with the accompanying table. In general, a heavily coated, mild steel welding rod should be used and the diameter of the electrode should not be greater than the tube wall thickness unless the operator increases the travel speed sufficiently to prevent overheating, undercutting and burning through the metal. The length of the arc should be held to approximately 1/8 inch. Polarity shall be as recommended by the electrode manufacturer or as found suitable for the specific work being accomplished. All tack welding and all weld endings shall be accomplished with the use of a crater

Arc Welding Electrode Requirements

Base Material	Thickness In Inches	Welding Rod					Amperage
		Material	Diameter Inches	Speci-fication	Arc Voltage		
Cm steel (4130 and X4130)	Up to .064 .064 to .078 .078 to .093	Plain carbon steel, heavily coated "Wilson 520," "G.E. W25," or "Airco 90"	1/16 5/64 3/32	10286-A GR. 5-E	17-20 17-21 17-21		20-40 25-60 30-80

Figure 1. Arc Welding Generator With Crater Eliminator.

eliminator if one is available. (See figure 1.) The small hole or crater at the weld end creates a stress concentration and a fatigue point and should therefore be eliminated if possible. The use of a crater eliminator will remedy this condition and a smooth weld end will result. (See figure 2.) Avoid rewelding as porosity in the weld may result. When a weld is built up by two or more beads or passes, the preceding weld must be cleaned free of scale or flux by chipping or scraping followed by brushing with a wire brush. Welding shall

not be dressed by removing metal from the joint unless further welding is to be done on the dressed region. Unless otherwise specified, the maximum width of welds for material thickness of not over 0.040 inch shall be ¼ inch. (See figure 3.) The depth of penetration shall be between 25 and 40 percent of the thickness of the base metal.

c. Oxyacetylene welding of steel. The oxyacetylene process is still considered the most flexible type of welding and generally best suited for repair work on aircraft. However, electric arc welding is acceptable, and repairs outlined will be applicable for either type of welding. Welding wire used for oxyacetylene welding of chrome molybdenum tubing must conform to Specification No. QQ-W-351, grade E. The torch tips should be of proper size for the thickness of the material to be welded. The following commonly used torch tip sizes are satisfactory:

Thickness of Steel	Diameter of Hole In Tip	Drill Size
0.015 to 0.031	0.026	71
0.031 to 0.065	0.031	68
0.065 to 0.125	0.037	63
0.125 to 0.188	0.042	58
0.188 to 0.250	0.055	54
0.250 to 0.375	0.067	51

For chrome molybdenum tubing of under 0.115 inch thickness the welding rod should be a plain copper-

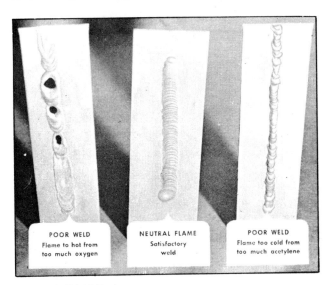

Figure 2. Weld Ends.

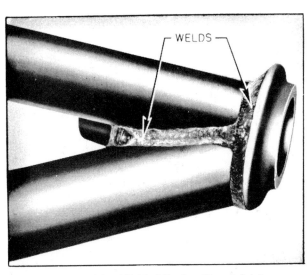

Figure 3. Typical Arc-Welded Engine Mount Joint.

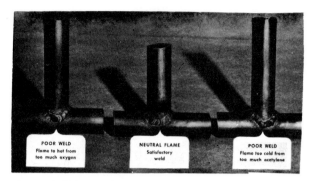

Figure 4. Types of Welds.

coated carbon steel, ¹⁄₁₆ inch or ³⁄₃₂-inch diameter rod; no flux is necessary. Preferably keep the flame pointed in the direction of welding in order to preheat the material. Maintain as neutral a flame as possible, for an excess of acetylene in the flame will carbonize the weld and an excess of oxygen will oxidize the weld. (See figure 4.) The feather part of the flame should not be more than 1½ times the length of the flame cone and not more than ⅛ inch long. Avoid rewelding, as overheating and porosity may result in the weld. At the end of the weld do not raise the torch suddenly from the weld, as this action may cause a pinhole in the weld. Welds shall not be dressed by removing metal from the joint unless further welding is to be done on the dressed region. If the thinnest of the tubes to be welded is less than 0.040 inch, the maximum width of the weld should not exceed ¼ inch. Standard commercial oxyacetylene welding equipment should be used. (See figure 5.)

d. Condition of completed welds. The finished weld should incorporate the following characteristics:

(1) The seam should be smooth and of uniform thickness.

(2) The weld should be built up to provide extra thickness at the seam.

(3) The weld metal should taper off smoothly into the base metal.

(4) No oxide should be formed on the base metal at a distance of more than ½ inch from the weld.

(5) The weld should show no signs of blowholes, porosity or projecting globules.

(6) The base metal should show no signs of pitting, burning, cracking or distortion.

(7) The beads shall be of correct size and number.

(8) The depth of penetration shall be sufficient to insure fusion of base metal and filler rod.

(9) Objectionable welding scale shall be removed by wire brushing or sandblasting.

e. Estimating extent of damage to steel tubes. When inspecting the fuselage truss for possible damage, the structure surrounding any visual damage must be carefully examined to insure that no secondary damage remains undetected. Secondary damage may be produced in some structure remote from the location of the primary damage by the transmission of the damaging stress along the tube. Damage of this nature usually occurs where the most abrupt change in load travel is experienced. If this damage remains unde-

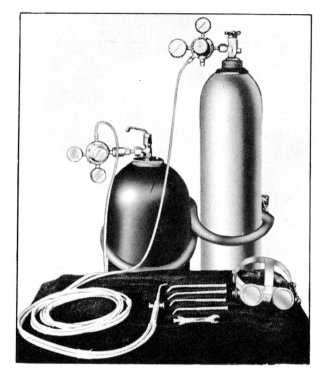

Figure 5. Oxyacetylene Welding Equipment.

tected, loads applied in the normal course of operation may cause failure of the part. Visually examine all joints for cracks, welding flaws, or failures. (See figure 6.)

f. Smooth dents in steel tubes. A minor smooth dent in steel tubing may often be removed by the following procedure: Remove one of the self-tapping screws provided at the extremities of the main steel tubes and apply an air pressure of upwards of 75 pounds per square inch to the inside of the steel truss. Heat the dented area evenly to a dull red with an acetylene torch until the internal air pressure forces out the dent and restores the original tube contour. If internal air pressure aand heat are not sufficient to remove the dent, tack weld a welding rod to the center of the dent and pull on the rod while heating the area. After the dent is removed, allow the area to cool and then release the internal air pressure. Replace the previously removed self-tapping screw.

CAUTION: Do not apply heat above a dull red to the middle third of the length of any tube.

---

g. Steel tube circumference bent to an oval shape. Where the circumference of a steel tube is bent to an oval shape, the area may be restored to normal in the cold condition by pressure exerted on the area through grooved steel form blocks. (See figure 7.) Drill a steel block to the diameter of the damaged tube then saw the block along the axis of the hole and separate the two sections of the block. Apply the two form block sections to the oval shaped area on the affected tube. Slip a heavy clamp over the blocks, tighten the clamp and exert pressure on the area until the oval shaped tube area is restored to the normal circular shape. (See figure 7.) If difficulty is encountered in shaping the tube

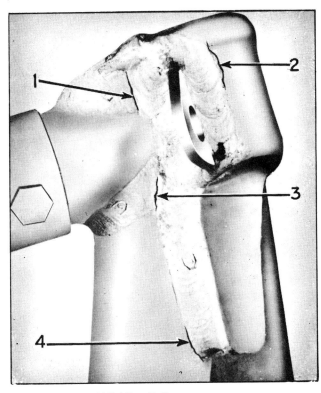

Figure 6. Typical Welding Failures.

in the cold condition, heat the area to a dull red then apply the steel blocks and clamp. Remove the clamp and the blocks. If the oval shaped area is longer than the length of the steel form blocks, reapply the form blocks and the clamp to successive affected areas until the entire length of the oval shaped area is restored to the normal circular shape.

h. Bowed steel tubes. Steel tubes which have been bowed without evidence of cracking may be straightened in the cold condition as shown. (See figure 8.) Cut three hardwood blocks grooved to fit the contour of the tube and line the grooves with leather or canvas. Obtain a length of channel iron equal to the length of the bow in the tube. Locate one of the grooved blocks at either extremity of the bow and apply the channel iron beam so that the beam spans the bowed area and backs up the two blocks. Apply the third block on the opposite side of the tube at the point of the maximum bend near the center of the bow. Slip one end of a heavy C-clamp over the channel iron beam and tighten the clamp down on the block at the center of the bend. In order to allow for springback of the tube, continue tightening the clamp until the tube is bent slightly in the opposite direction. (See figure 8.) Remove the clamp and the blocks. Check the alignment of the tube by placing an accurate straightedge on both the side and the top of the tube. If the straightedge check reveals a slight bow in the tube, reapply the blocks and the clamp and check until the tube lines up with a straightedge in both reference planes. If cracks appear at the point where the maximum bow was corrected, drill a No. 40 (0.098) hole at the ends of the crack and weld a split steel sleeve over the area as outlined in the paragraph k. "Sharp Dents or Cracks in Lengths of Steel Tubes." In every case where a bent tube is restored, carefully test all adjacent welding joints for cracks, and repair the cracks.

i. Small cracks at steel tubing cluster joints. If it is necessary to check an individual tubing joints for cracks, apply a liberal coat of light oil to the affected area, thoroughly wipe the oil from the joint, and then spray a coat of whiting (a mixture of chalk and alcohol). A crack in the joint will usually be shown by the appearance of oil on the whiting from the crack recess. (See figure 7.) After whiting, remove all finish from the area by rubbing with steel wool or a wire brush. If the crack is located in an original weld bead, carefully chip, file, or grind out the existing weld bead, and reweld over the crack along the original weld line. When grinding off the original weld bead, take particular care to avoid removing any of the existing tube or gusset material. If the crack is near a cluster joint but away from the original weld bead, remove the finish from the area with steel wool, drill a No. 40 (0.098) hole at the ends of the crack, and weld an overlapping doubler over the area. No more than two cracks should be repaired in the same general area. At the conclusion of the repair, apply one coat of zinc chromate primer to the area from which the finish was previously removed. Apply finish coats to match the adjacent surface.

j. Sharp dents at a steel tube cluster joint. Sharp dents at a steel tube cluster joint may be repaired by welding an especially formed steel patch plate over the dented area and surrounding tubes. (See figure 9.) To prepare the patch plate, cut a section of steel plate of a thickness equal to or greater than that of the damaged tube. Trim the reinforcing plate (figure 9) so that

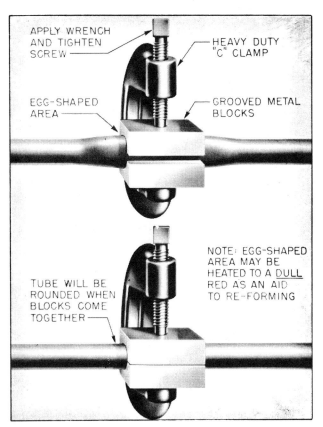

Figure 7. Correcting Oval-Shaped Steel Tube Distortion.

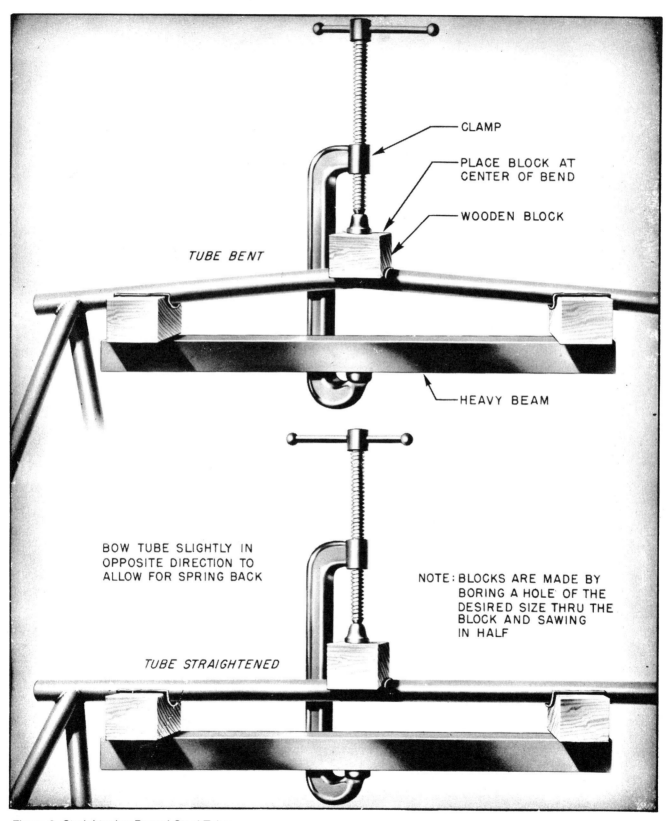

CLAMP

PLACE BLOCK AT
CENTER OF BEND

WOODEN BLOCK

TUBE BENT

HEAVY BEAM

BOW TUBE SLIGHTLY IN
OPPOSITE DIRECTION TO
ALLOW FOR SPRING BACK

NOTE: BLOCKS ARE MADE BY
BORING A HOLE OF THE
DESIRED SIZE THRU THE
BLOCK AND SAWING
IN HALF

TUBE STRAIGHTENED

Figure 8. Straightening Bowed Steel Tubes.

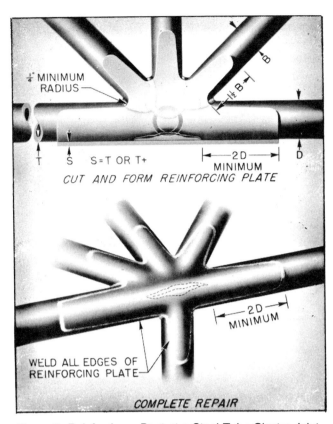

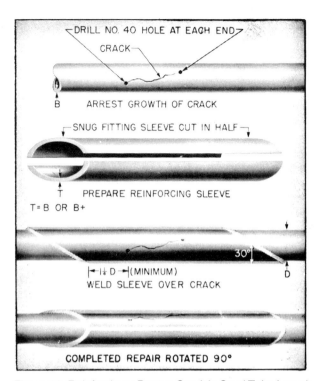

Figure 9. Reinforcing a Dent at a Steel Tube Cluster Joint.

Figure 10. Reinforcing a Dent or Crack in Steel Tube Length.

the plate extends a minimum of two times the diameter of the tube from the nearest edge of the dent and over adjacent tubes 1½ times the diameter of the tube. On the damaged cluster joint area to be covered by the reinforcing plate, rub off all the existing finish with steel wool. The reinforcing plate may be formed before any welding is attempted, or the plate may be cut and tack-welded to one or more of the tubes forming the cluster joint, then heated and pounded around the joint contour as required to produce a smooth contour. Avoid unnecessary heating of the reinforcing plate while forming, but apply sufficient heat and pound the plate so that there is generally a gap of no more than ¹/₁₆ inch from the contour of the joint to the reinforcing plate. While forming the plate, exercise care to prevent damage at the apex of the angle formed by any two adjacent fingers of the plate. After the reinforcing plate is formed and tack-welded to the cluster joint, weld the plate edges to the cluster joint.

k. Sharp dents or cracks in lengths of steel tubes. If a crack appears in a length of steel tube, usually as the result of previously straightening the tube, first drill a No. 40 (0.098) hole at the ends of the crack and then rub the area with steel wool to remove the finish around the tube for a distance of approximately three inches on each side of the damage. (See figure 10.) If the damage is in the form of a sharp dent which cannot be removed by any of the methods previously outlined, remove the finish in the same manner. In order to reinforce the dented or the cracked area, select a length of a spare steel tube sleeve having an inside diameter approximately equal to the outside diameter of the

damaged tube and of the same wall thickness. Diagonally cut the steel sleeve reinforcement at a 30° angle on both ends so that the distance of the sleeve from the edge of the crack or dent is not less than 1¼ times the diameter of the damaged tube. (See figure 14.) Cut through the entire length of the reinforcing sleeve and separate the half sections of the sleeve. Clamp the two sleeve sections to the proper positions on the affected areas of the original steel tube. Weld the reinforcing sleeve along the length of the two sides, and weld both ends of the sleeve to the damaged steel tube as shown.

Splicing Of Structural Tubes

a. General. Tubular members of the fuselage truss may be spliced by partial tube replacement used with internal or external reinforcing steel sleeves, or by the use of an externally telescoping tube replacement of the next larger diameter tubing. Each type of splice has its particular advantage or function and the methods involved are essentially the same. All splicing is accomplished with electric arc welding or oxyacetylene welding. If the original damaged tube accommodates castings or fittings which have been fabricated to fit the tube contour, the spliced replacement tube must be of the same diameter. If no such fittings are applied to the original damaged tube, the externally telescoping splice replacement may be used. Two types of splice welds are permitted, the diagonal and the fishmouth. Being the stronger of the two, the fishmouth splice weld is preferred to the diagonal. However, the nature and location of the damage will determine which type must be used. Splices may not be made in the middle third of a tube section and only one partial replacement tube can be inserted in any one

75

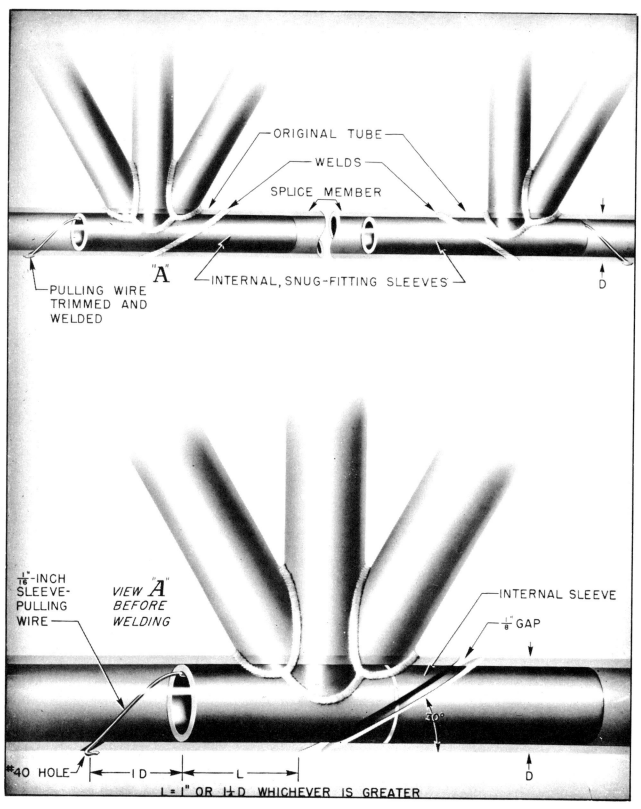

ORIGINAL TUBE

WELDS

SPLICE MEMBER

"A"

PULLING WIRE
TRIMMED AND
WELDED

INTERNAL, SNUG-FITTING SLEEVES

D

$\frac{1}{16}$"-INCH
SLEEVE-
PULLING
WIRE

VIEW "A"
BEFORE
WELDING

INTERNAL SLEEVE

$\frac{1}{8}$" GAP

30°

#40 HOLE

ID

L

D

l = I" OR I½D WHICHEVER IS GREATER

Figure 11. Steel Tube Inner Sleeve Splice.

section of a structural member. If a member is damaged at a joint so that it is impossible to retain a stub to which another member can be attached, replace the tube if it is a web member; and if the tube is a continuous longeron, locate the splice in the adjacent section.

Misalignment of a tubular structure due to contraction and expansion of the metal during welding can be prevented by using wood braces with notches in the ends to hold the tubes in position. When new tubes are used to replace bent or damaged tubes, the original align-

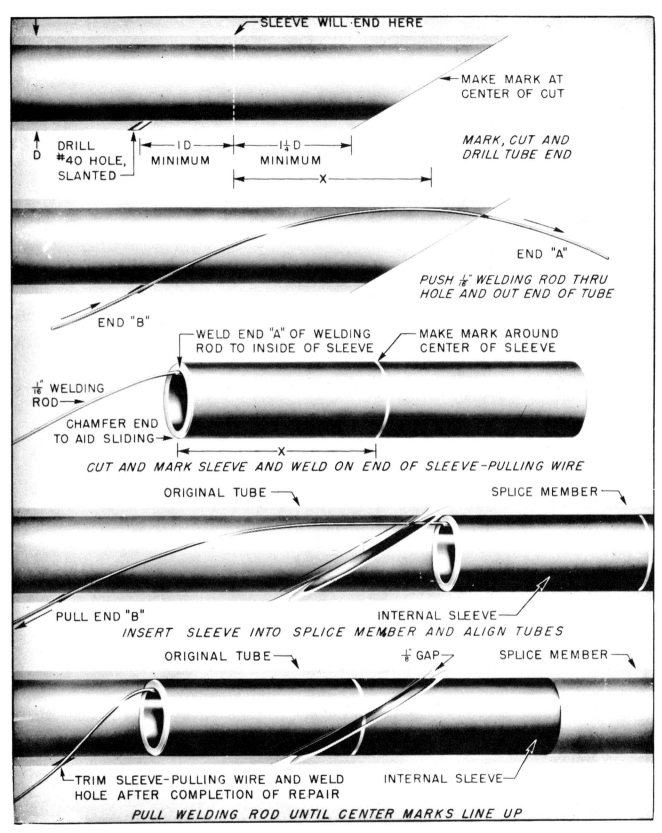

SLEEVE WILL END HERE

MAKE MARK AT
CENTER OF CUT

MARK, CUT AND
DRILL TUBE END

DRILL
#40 HOLE,
SLANTED

|← ID MINIMUM →|← 1¼ D MINIMUM →|

|←——— X ———→|

D

END "A"

PUSH ⅟₁₆" WELDING ROD THRU
HOLE AND OUT END OF TUBE

END "B"

WELD END "A" OF WELDING
ROD TO INSIDE OF SLEEVE

MAKE MARK AROUND
CENTER OF SLEEVE

⅟₁₆" WELDING
ROD

CHAMFER END
TO AID SLIDING

|←——— X ———→|

CUT AND MARK SLEEVE AND WELD ON END OF SLEEVE-PULLING WIRE

ORIGINAL TUBE

SPLICE MEMBER

PULL END "B"

INTERNAL SLEEVE

INSERT SLEEVE INTO SPLICE MEMBER AND ALIGN TUBES

ORIGINAL TUBE

⅛" GAP

SPLICE MEMBER

INTERNAL SLEEVE

TRIM SLEEVE-PULLING WIRE AND WELD
HOLE AFTER COMPLETION OF REPAIR

PULL WELDING ROD UNTIL CENTER MARKS LINE UP

Figure 12. Centering Inner Sleeve in Steel Tube.

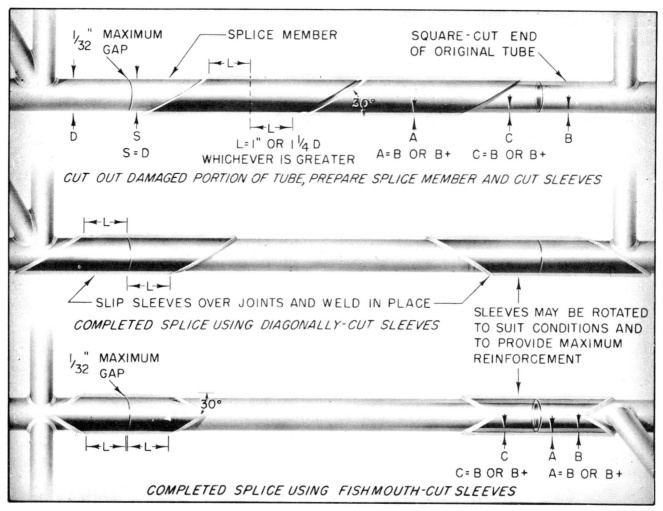

Figure 13. Steel Tube Outer Sleeve Splice.

ment of the structure must be maintained and checked. This can be done by measuring the distance between points of corresponding members on undamaged aircraft.

CAUTION: Make no splice by butt welding any member between station points.

---

b. Splicing of structural tube by inner sleeve method. If the damage to a structural tube is such that partial replacement of the tube is necessary, the inner sleeve splice is recommended, especially where a smooth tube surface is desired. (See figure 11.) Diagonally cut out the damaged portion of the tube with a hacksaw, locating the cuts away from the middle third of the affected tube section. Remove the burr from the edges of the cuts by filing. Diagonally cut a replacement steel tube to match the diameter, wall thickness, and length of the removed portion of the damaged tube. At each end of the replacement tube allow a ⅛ inch gap from the diagonal cuts to the stubs of the original tube. Select a length of steel tubing of the same wall thickness and of an outside diameter approximately equal to the inside diameter of the damaged tube. This inner sleeve tube material should fit snugly within the original tube, with a maximum tolerance of ¹⁄₆₄ inch.

From this inner sleeve tube material cut two sections of tubing, each of such a length that the ends of the inner sleeve will be a minimum distance of 1¼ tube diameters from the nearest end of the diagonal cut. (See figure 11.) Dip the replacement tube and the inner sleeves into hot 74° C (165° F) raw linseed oil; then wipe the oil from the outer circumference of the tubes. Make a mark on the outside of the diagonally cut original tube stub midway along the diagonal cut. (See figure 12.) At a minimum distance of 2¼ times the tube diameter, measured from the nearest end of the diagonal cut, center punch the tube, and start drilling the No. 40 hole at a 90° angle. After a shallow hole is started from which the drill will not jump out, slant the drill toward the cut and drill at a 30° angle. Slanting the hole in this manner aligns the edges of the hole with the line of pull of the sleeve-pulling wire, and prevents the wire from scraping the hole edges. Remove the burr from the edges of the hole with a round, needle-point file. Obtain a length of ¹⁄₁₆ inch welding or brazing wire, insert one end into the drilled hole and push the wire out the end of the tube. (See figure 12.) Weld the end of the wire to the inner side of the reinforcing sleeve. Chamfer the end of the sleeve as an aid in sliding the tube into position. With thin paint, metal dye, or emery paper, make a narrow mark around the center of the reinforcing sleeve. Slip the sleeve into the re-

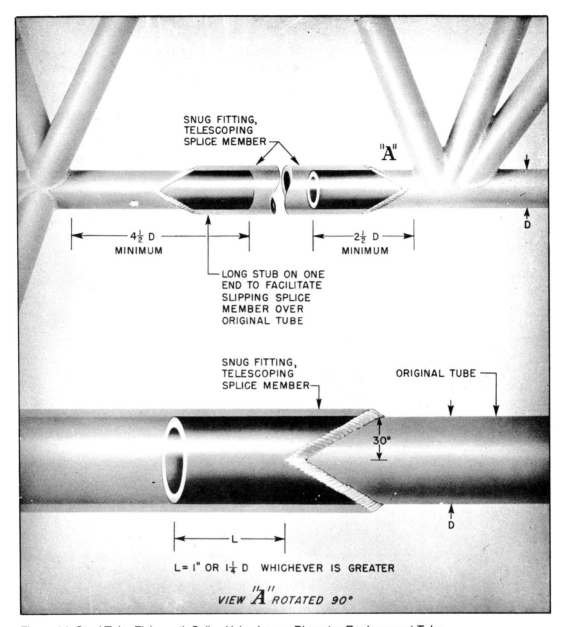

SNUG FITTING,
TELESCOPING
SPLICE MEMBER

"A"

4½ D
MINIMUM

2½ D
MINIMUM

D

LONG STUB ON ONE
END TO FACILITATE
SLIPPING SPLICE
MEMBER OVER
ORIGINAL TUBE

SNUG FITTING,
TELESCOPING
SPLICE MEMBER

ORIGINAL TUBE

30°

D

L

L = I" OR I¼ D WHICHEVER IS GREATER

VIEW *A* ROTATED 90°

Figure 14. Steel Tube Fishmouth Splice Using Larger Diameter Replacement Tube.

placement tube so that the welded wire is 180° from the drilled hole. If the inner sleeve fits very tightly in the replacement tube, chill the sleeve with dry ice or in cold water. If this is insufficient, polish down the diameter of the sleeve with emery cloth. The contraction of the inner sleeve by chilling or by polishing allows more clearance from the inner sleeve to the inside wall of the tube stubs. Align the original tube stubs with the replacement tube. Pull on the exposed end of the sleeve-pulling wire until the center mark on the sleeve is directly in line with the center mark on the diagonal cut. (See figure 12.) When this occurs, the inner sleeve is centered beneath the joint. Sharply bend the pulling wire over to hold the sleeve in position. At each side of the replacement tube, weld the inner sleeve to the tube stubs through the ⅛ inch gap between the stubs. (See figure 12.) Completely fill the ⅛ inch gap and form a weld bead over the gap. After the joint is welded, snip off the pulling wire flush with the surface of the tube and weld over the hole.

c. Splicing structural tube by outer sleeve method. If partial replacement of a tube is necessary, an outer sleeve splice may be used, where conditions warrant, as an alternate splice to the inner sleeve splice and the splice using a larger diameter replacement tube. However, the outer sleeve splice requires the greatest amount of welding; and therefore, it should be used only where the other splicing methods are not suitable. Squarely cut out the damaged section of the tube, locating the cuts away from the middle third of the tube section. Cut a replacement steel tube section to match the outside diameter, wall thickness, and length of the removed tube. This replacement tube must bear against the stubs of the original tube with a total tolerance not to exceed ¹⁄₃₂ inch. Dip the replacement tube into hot 74° C (165° F) raw linseed oil; then wipe the oil from the outer circumference of the tube. Select a length of steel tubing of an inside diameter approximately equal to the outside diameter of the damaged tube and of the same wall thickness. This outer sleeve tube material should fit snugly about the original tube with a maximum tolerance of 1/64 inch. From this outer sleeve tube material, cut two sections of tubing diagonally or fishmouth, each of such a length that the nearest ends of the outer sleeve are a minimum distance of 1¼ tube diameters from the ends of the cut on the original tube. (See figure 13.) Use a fishmouth-cut sleeve wherever possible. Remove the burr from all the edges of the sleeves, replacement tube, and original tube stubs. Slip the two sleeves over the replacement tube, line up the replacement tube with the original tube stubs, and slip the sleeves out over the center of each joint. (See figure 13.) Adjust the sleeves to suit the area and to provide maximum reinforcement. Tack weld the two sleeves to the replacement tube in two places before welding. Apply a uniform weld around both ends of one of the reinforcing sleeves and allow the weld to cool. Then weld around both ends of the remaining reinforcing tube. (See figure 13.) Allow one sleeve weld to cool before welding the remaining tube, to prevent undue warping.

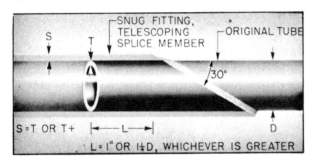

Figure 15. Steel Tube Diagonal Splice Using Larger Diameter Replacement Tube.

d. Splicing structural tubes using larger diameter replacement tubes. This method of splicing structural tubes requires the least amount of cutting and welding. However, this splicing method cannot be used where the damaged tube is cut too near the adjacent cluster joints or where bracket mounting provisions make it necessary to maintain the same replacement tube diameter as the original. As an aid in installing the replacement tube, squarely cut the original damaged tube, leaving a minimum short stud equal to 2½ tube diameters on one end and a minimum long stub equal to 4½ tube diameters on the other end. (See figure 14.) The cuts must be away from the middle third of the affected tube. Select a spare length of steel tubing having an inside diameter approximately equal to the outside diameter of the damaged tube and of the same wall thickness as or greater than the damaged tube. This replacement tube material should fit snugly about the original tube with a maximum tolerance of 1/64 inch. From this replacement tube material, diagonally or fishmouth, cut a section of tubing of such a length that each end of the tube is a minimum distance of 1¼ tube diameters from the end of the cut on the original tube. Use a fishmouth-cut replacement tube wherever possible. (See figure 14.) However, a diagonally cut tube may also be used. (See figure 15.) Remove the burr from the edges of the replacement tube and the original tube stubs. If a fishmouth cut is used, file out the sharp

radius of the cut with a small, round file. Dip the replacement tube into hot, 74° C (165° F), raw linseed oil; then wipe the oil from the outer circumference of the tube. Spring the long stub of the original tube from the normal position; slip the replacement tube over the long stub, then back over the short stub. Center the replacement tube between the stubs of the original tube. In several places tack-weld one end of the replacement tube; then weld completely around the end. In order to prevent distortion, allow the weld to cool completely; then weld the remaining end of the replacement tube to the original tube. (See figure 14.)

e. Replacing structural tubes. If tubes are severely damaged, replace them. Tube replacement is necessary where an original tube stub is too short to attach a replacement and where splice welds will be made in the middle third of a member. When it is necessary to remove a member at a joint or from a cluster of tubes, use a fine-toothed hacksaw and remove the tube carefully and completely from the structure. While cutting out the tube, exercise caution to prevent any damage to adjacent tubes or welds. Where new welds are to be made over the location of existing welds upon the insertion of the new member, completely chip or file off the old welds. Dip the replacement tube into hot 74° (C (165° F) raw linseed oil then wipe the oil from the outer circumference of the tube. When installing a new tube member, allow a clearance of 1/32 inch at either end for expansion. Unless a welding jig is available, the actual process of welding should be accomplished in as systematic a manner as possible pertinent to the application of heat and the resultant possible distortion. After the new tube has been welded in place, clean the welded joints with a wire brush or steel wool.

Magnafluxing Of Metals

a. General. The magnaflux method of inspection is a nondestructive test to reveal the presence of hidden cracks, seams, laps, slag inclusions and similar defects which cannot be detected visually. Results obtained by magnaflux inspection are relative and many defects of little or no consequence will be found along with those of importance. In case of doubt, it is better to reject a part than to take a chance on its soundness.

A Home-Made 'Sand Blaster'

Anyone who has ever cleaned paint and rust off an old steel tubing airplane structure knows what a boon a good sand-blasting machine would be. Sometimes you can find one in a city, but even then it's a problem whether or not its owners can or will handle a job the size of a fuselage. For many, a sand-blaster is as far away as the moon.

Shown here are drawings for rigging up one of your own at modest cost. The prime requirements are a source of suitable sand and a compressor large enough for the job. Manufacturers of commercial sand-blasting equipment sell special grit, but you can get by with common dry sand sifted through insect screening. Any industrial compressor of the size commonly used at gasoline stations and aircraft repair shops will do well. This would be something on the order of a machine delivering 14 cu. ft. of air per minute at 80 lbs. pressure, although a smaller one might do if it has a generous size storage tank. Don't waste time trying to make a little one-butterfly-power portable compressor do the work.

The drawings are practically self-explanatory. The reason why air is led into the top of the sand tank is to equalize pressure on the top and bottom of the sand. Without this feature, air would simply blow up through the sand like a geyser and nothing would flow down to the nozzle. The stopper at the top (Detail A) can be made of almost anything you might hit upon, the main requirement being that it have a good wedging action. An old valve from a big airplane engine might work, if fitted with a guide and rubber "O" ring for a seat. The tank itself could be adapted from a surplus aviation oxygen tank. When the tank is finished, use an automobile tire pump or airplane shock strut to fill it with

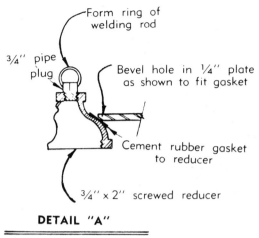

DETAIL "A"

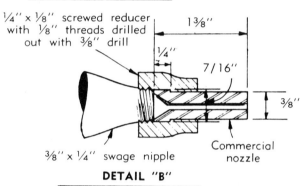

DETAIL "B"

Drawings by Robert McRoberts

air to about 50 percent above normal pressure for a safety check.

All welding and threading must be of good quality. Take off any sharp edges. Clean out chips from the threading work. Do the welding before installing the gasket and sealer material. The valve at the bottom of the tank must be of the gate type for anything else will jam with sand. Buy 3/32 in. standard steel lettering nozzles from an industrial supply house, or a monument works. You can make up your own nozzles from rod stock, too.

Close the sand valve in the bottom to prevent clogging the pipes, and fill the tank with sand almost to the level of the top air inlet. Shake down any grains left on the filler plug or its gasket. Close the nozzle petcock. Open the air shut-off valve, aim the nozzle at the work and open the nozzle petcock. Adjust the sand valve to get a good flow . . . too much sand may cause clogging. To prevent the sand from piling up in the hose, shut the sand off before closing the nozzle valve. Goggles are essential when using the machine. Don't point the nozzle too long at any one spot on the work, especially where thin stock is concerned. Do the work out-of-doors as flying sand will cover everything in a shop. Wear heavy work gloves and, preferably, coveralls that will keep most of the sand from filling your clothes.

by Ron Scott

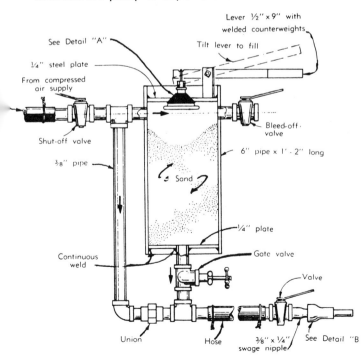

Typical Design Details

Various deficiencies in design are covered in the following drawings. These drawings were selected because of the important lessons which they teach. A visual presentation is used to better focus attention on troublesome items which have occurred in service.

It will be noted that the design lessons are premised on specific cases. Even so, they are often applicable to other details, or other systems or portions of the aircraft. Accordingly, it is suggested that the designer study all of the drawings in order to attain their widest possible application towards improvement in design.

Service experience shows a critical need for improved detailed design of steel tubular joints, footings, and splices. Accordingly, the following examples, taken from authoritative texts on recommended design practice, are here presented.

DON'T

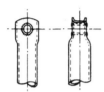

BAD — This type of end is subject to failure as a result of grinding or machining at the ends of the spacer tube.

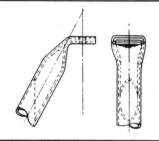

BAD — This type of pinched end, even with suitable reinforcing sleeve, is prone to crack at the bend as a result of cold-working in manufacture or fatigue in service.

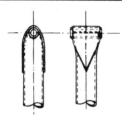

BAD — This type of end is not so strong in compression as would appear. In heavy service, it fails by crushing under the spacer tube.

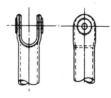

BAD — This type of end requires an excessive amount of cold-working and too many welding operations.

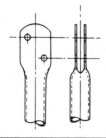

BAD — This type of end has unsatisfactory resistance to fatigue and moments generated by local eccentricity.

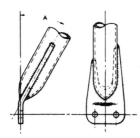

GOOD — This type of end is considered satisfactory up to an angle of bend of 30°. Beyond this angle, eccentricity on the attaching bolts becomes seriously objectionable. Care should be taken to avoid termination of welding at opposite ends of the same section of the tube.

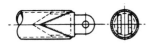

GOOD — This welded plug end has been generally satisfactory. Sudden changes of cross section should be prevented by notching the tube and shaping the concealed portion of the plug. Care should be taken to prevent boring the inside of the end deep enough to weaken the end.

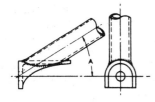

GOOD — This type of tube end has been satisfactory as a coupling for engine mounts. If angle A does not exceed 30°, this joint may match the tensile strength of the tube. Eccentricity with respect to the bolt is easily prevented through a wide range of angles.

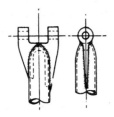

GOOD — This type of end is considered satisfactory where a wide hinge is required. The angle of the hinge axis with respect to the tube axis may be varied over a wide range.

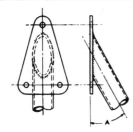

GOOD — These types of ends are generally satisfactory where a fixed end condition is desired.

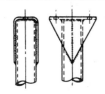

GOOD — These types of ends are generally satisfactory where a fixed end condition is desired.

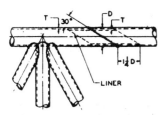

GOOD — Tube splices should be made on 30° angles. Fish-mouth splices may be used where length is to be saved but are less desirable than the simple scarf splices, because they bring two welded areas at the same section of the tubing. Splices should be butted or flush as the welding is more reliable from an edge to an edge than from an edge to a surface. In all cases, a tubular liner should be used, extending beyond the welding at least 1 inch or 1¼ D, whichever is the greater. This prevents reduction of diameter taking place under tension and consequently raises the tensile strength of the splice. The liner also serves to aline the tube ends for the welding operation.

Structural failures of fittings and parts often can be attributed to improper selection of materials at the time of original design. One serious structural failure studied was partially attributable to the use of SAE 1012 steel in the end fittings of certain wing lift-struts. This material is subject to brittle failure at ordinary or low temperature; consequently, it is unsuitable for vital parts. Several other serious structural failures were attributed mainly to the use of special aluminum alloys having high ultimate and yield strengths but relatively low fatigue strengths. The particular failures were due to fatigue which occurred at relatively low periods of service life. There are several cases wherein connecting hoses have deteriorated, become swollen and burst, because of the adverse chemical effects of insecticide materials which they carried. Obviously the use, for critical parts, of materials whose characteristics have not been reasonably well established or which are not suitable for the particular service conditions should be avoided.

Welding of Ferrous Materials

Principles of Welding Design. Welded joints can best resist compression and shear stresses, but are often undesirable for pure tension and tension due to bending. Numerous service difficulties and failures have attributed to the existence of the following conditions which should be avoided whenever possible:

(a) A joint between relatively thin and thick gauges of material. The heat required to bring the thicker material up to the welding temperature may burn or melt away the thin material.

(b) The convergence of more than six members to form a welded cluster. The repeated and prolonged applications of heat on the small area where the members meet tend to weaken the base metal adjacent to the weld material.

(c) The use of tin-lead solder in proximity to a joint. A subsequent repair of the joint might cause contamination of the weld metal by the solder.

(d) The welding of a brazed joint. If welded repairs are subsequently made in the field, complete removal of brazing material prior to welding is very difficult because the brazing alloy can penetrate the base metal for a considerable distance. Visually, the joint will appear clean; actually, it may be contaminated by the brazing alloy and be unfit for welding. The reverse practice of brazing a welded joint is permissible provided that necessary strength is attained.

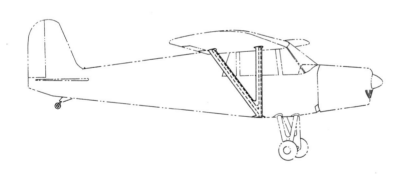

Attachment of a Wing Lift Strut Fairing.

DESIGN DEFICIENCY

The fittings attaching the streamline fairings to the round tubular lift struts became loosened, and vibrational movement caused the fittings to wear into the lift struts, thus materially weakening them.

RECOMMENDATION

The attachment of the streamline fairings to the lift struts should be made positive and of rugged design.

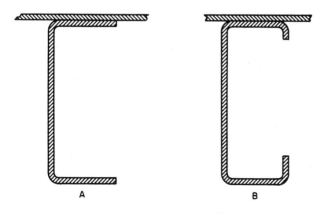

A   B

Desirable Structural Shapes.

DESIGN DEFICIENCY

Free edge sections, such as shown in detail A, are inefficient structurally. If unprotected in service, the free edges may be bent, thereby reducing their original strength.

RECOMMENDATION

Depending upon the particular installation, curved edge sections as in detail B, should be used in preference to the free edge section shown in detail A.

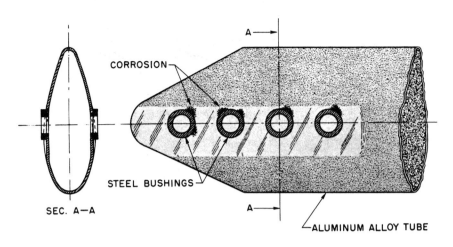

SEC. A—A

CORROSION

STEEL BUSHINGS

ALUMINUM ALLOY TUBE

Corrosion of a Wing Lift Strut End Fitting.

DESIGN DEFICIENCY

Steel bushings are used in an aluminum alloy wing lift strut fitting for a seaplane. Due to a lack of surface protection, electrolytic corrosion occurred in the strut adjacent to the steel bushing. Corrosion also occurred due to salt-water spray.

RECOMMENDATION

Corrosion protective paint or plating should be used and frequent periodic inspections should be conducted. (Corrosion due to salt-water spray can be considerably retarded if the aircraft is given a thorough washing with fresh water while beached.)

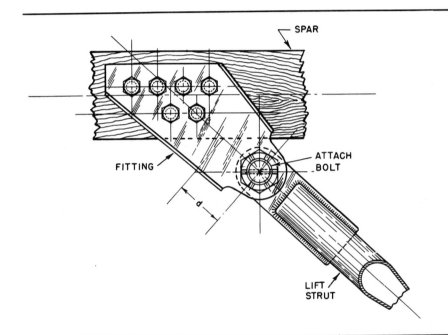

SPAR

FITTING

ATTACH BOLT

d

LIFT STRUT

Wing Lift Strut-to-Spar Attachment Fitting.

DESIGN DEFICIENCY

The fitting plates are somewhat weak in bending in a fore-and-aft direction. When the lift strut is in compression, the plates will flex. This is conducive to bending-fatigue failure of the plates.

RECOMMENDATION

The fitting plates should be made more rigid in bending in a fore-and-aft direction, and the overhang portion (dimension d) should be reduced as much as possible.

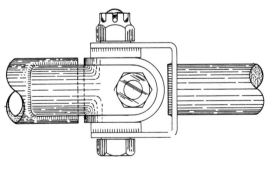

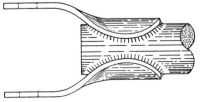

Universal Joint

DESIGN DEFICIENCY

Welding of the solid shaft to the relatively thin plate was conducive to a cold weld. Also, there was an insufficient length of weld.

THE FIX

The critical weld detail was revised to incorporate a greater length of weld as shown in the lower sketch. In addition, in order to reduce the possibility of a cold weld, special precautions were taken to have the local portion of the solid shaft at a sufficiently high temperature during the welding process.

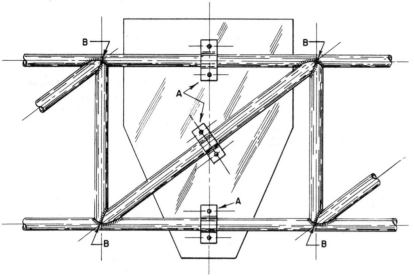

Transmittal of Loads to the Primary Structure.

DESIGN DEFICIENCY

Concentrated loads are transmitted to the primary structure at the midspans of bays, as at points *A*. This induces bending in the tubular members, which was not taken into account in the original design.

RECOMMENDATION

Concentrated loads should be transmitted to the panel points *B*, either directly or through relatively stiff intermediate structure. If this is not practicable, the effects of the induced bending should be considered in design.

Grinding or Machining Welded Material in a Welded Joint.

DESIGN DEFICIENCY

Shown (right hand sketch) is a typical fitting which incorporates an edge-welded end tube. The end tube was first edge-welded and subsequently machine-faced or ground to fit a mating part. This causes serious weakening of the weld.

RECOMMENDATION

Do not machine, grind, wire-brush, or file welded material. The left hand sketch shows a design preferable to that shown in the right hand sketch since the original edge weld is intact.

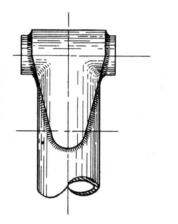
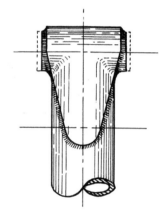

Welded Gussets in an Engine Mount.

DESIGN DEFICIENCY

The welded joints of the center gusset had an undue tendency to crack. The cause was attributed to an eccentricity resulting from differences in size of the gussets.

THE FIX

The center gusset was enlarged to eliminate the apparent eccentricity.

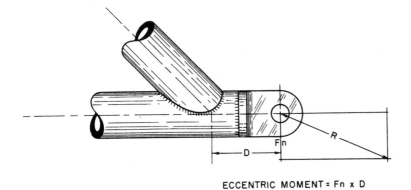

ECCENTRIC MOMENT = Fn x D

Eccentric Joint.

DESIGN DEFICIENCY
The eccentric joint is subject to engine vibration and the effect of the eccentricity was not considered in the original design.

RECOMMENDATION
Eccentric joints should be avoided. If this is not practicable, the effect of the eccentricity should be considered in design. Gussets or finger patches may be necessary for additional reinforcement.

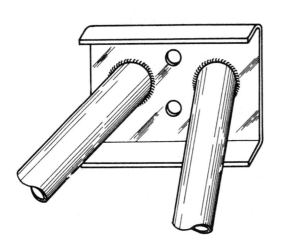

Welded Engine-Mount Fitting.

DESIGN DEFICIENCY
This engine-mount pad is eccentrically loaded and it is relatively flexible in comparison to the tube. Under load, the bending stresses caused cracking of the welds.

RECOMMENDATION
The butt-welded attachment of flat plates and pads at the ends of tubes should be avoided. The type of end fitting shown on page 83 (illustration second from bottom) appears more desirable.

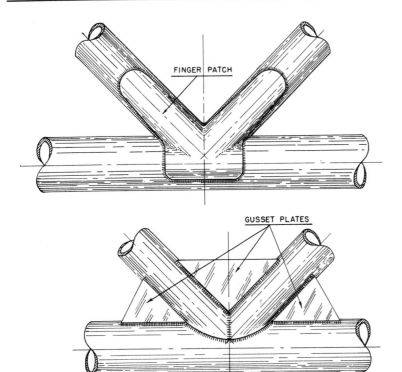

FINGER PATCH

GUSSET PLATES

Welded Joint in an Engine Mount.

DESIGN DEFICIENCY
Failures often occur in plain welded joints of tubular engine mounts, as these invariably are highly stressed and are subject to vibration. Welds in tension are particularly vulnerable in this regard.

RECOMMENDATION
Plain welded joints in tubular engine mounts should be avoided. Welded finger patches or gusset plates should be used for added reinforcements, as shown.

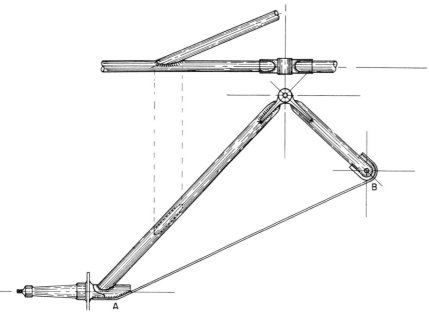

Landing Gear Structure.

DESIGN DEFICIENCY

The ends of the strap (A-B) are eccentric, consequently when it is under load, both tensile and bending stresses occur at its welded ends. The strap has a tendency to vibrate during both ground and flight maneuvers and this also induces bending stresses at the welds. The welded ends of the strap are inherently vulnerable to bending and fatigue stresses. In some cases, poor welding accentuated the aforementioned deficiencies. (Questions concerning the attachment of the axle to the strut are covered on page 92 (Landing Gear Axle).

RECOMMENDATION

Satisfactory strength of the welded ends of the strap can probably best be attained by increasing the width of the strap at its ends.

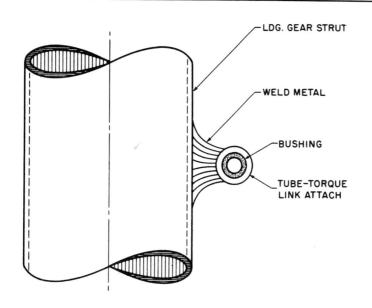

LDG. GEAR STRUT

WELD METAL

BUSHING

TUBE-TORQUE
LINK ATTACH

Welded Attachment of a Bushing to a Landing Gear Strut.

DESIGN DEFICIENCY

During fabrication, the bushing support tube and the strut are positioned in a jig. Weld material is then built up to fill the space between them. Failures have occurred in the weld material and at the strut due to tearing out of the wall material adjacent to the weld. The latter failure is attributed to the adverse effects of prolonged heating in building up the necessary weld material.

RECOMMENDATION

An excessive buildup of weld material in welding assemblies should be avoided

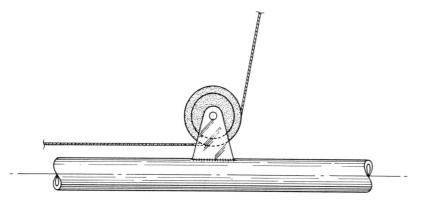

Welded Attachment of a Pulley Bracket.

DESIGN DEFICIENCY

The welded fitting is subjected mainly to tension. Welds can best resist shear and compressive loadings, and are often unsuited for tension loadings.

RECOMMENDATION

If the tension loading of welded fittings cannot be avoided, considerable excess strength relative to the tensile component of the design load should be provided.

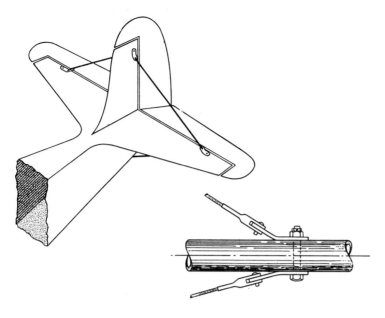

Stabilizer Tie Rod Attachment Fitting.

DESIGN DEFICIENCY

The tie rod is fabricated from plain aircraft wire and the lug is fabricated from steel sheet. Vibration of the tie rod caused a bending stress concentration and fatigue failure in the sharp **V**-thread at the end of the terminal. The lugs are eccentrically loaded and the resultant bending and vibration and fatigue caused their failure at relatively low periods of service life.

THE FIX

The terminal was lengthened to extend considerably beyond the threaded portion of the tie rod, thus eliminating bending due to vibration in the sharp **V**-thread. An extra large diameter washer was inserted under the head and nut of each bolt, thus imparting necessary support to the lugs.

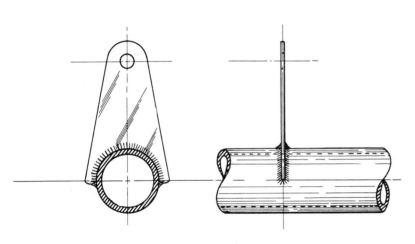

Welded Attachment of a Torque Tube Horn.

DESIGN DEFICIENCY

The flat-plate type horn is welded to the torque tube on both its sides. The horn is relatively thin, consequently welding on both its sides tends to burn the material and weaken the attachment. The horn is relatively weak against lateral and buckling loads.

RECOMMENDATION

In welded assemblies of the type shown, relatively thin material should be welded on only one side to avoid possible burning of the material. It is presumed, of course, that the strength of a single weld is adequate. The horn should be strengthened to resist loads in a lateral direction.

Rudder Stops.

DESIGN DEFICIENCY

Loads resulting from banging of the rudder against the stops were particularly severe. The conditions were aggravated by a slight misalinement of the stops during their welded assembly. Plain butt-welding does not afford an attachment of sufficient ruggedness.

RECOMMENDATION

Control surface stops should be more ruggedly designed, eliminating the butt-welded attachment of the stops, if possible. If attachment is by welding, the welds preferably should be loaded in shear instead of bending.

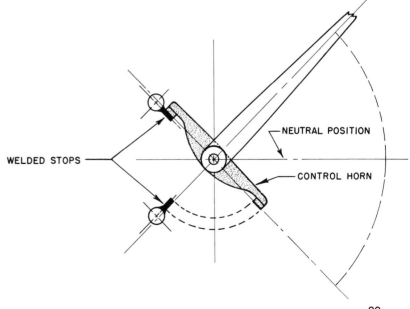

NEUTRAL POSITION

WELDED STOPS

CONTROL HORN

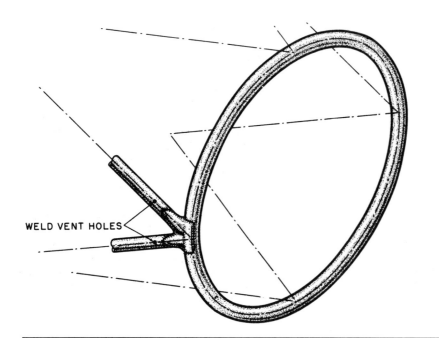

WELD VENT HOLES

Vent Holes in an Engine Mount.

DESIGN DEFICIENCY

Welding of the engine mount during its manufacture necessitates the use of weld vent holes. These holes had been filled by drivescrews, which resulted in stress concentration and fatigue failure of the tubes at the vent holes.

THE FIX

The drivescrews were omitted and the weld vent holes were filled by arc or heli-arc welding with air cooling. This eliminated failure in the lower tubes. Additional, although infrequent, failures of the upper tubes were eventually eliminated by changing to larger tubes.

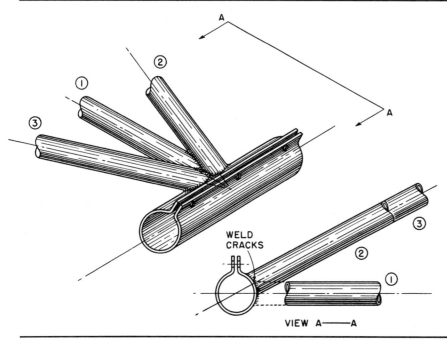

A
①
②
③
A

WELD CRACKS
③
②
①

VIEW A——A

Welded Clamps in a Tubular Engine Mount.

DESIGN DEFICIENCY

There is shown one of four attachment points for an engine mount of a helicopter. The tubes are butt-welded to the clamp. The clamp plate is flexible relative to the adjacent tubular structure, and flexing of the clamp results in stress concentration and eventual failure of the weld due to fatigue. In one of the specimens examined, the quality of the welding appeared inferior.

RECOMMENDATION

The joint should be redesigned using instead one of the footings depicted generally on page 93.

Wing Lift Strut-to-Fuselage Attachment Fitting.

DESIGN DEFICIENCY

The radius R is too small, and cracking occurred during fabrication of the particular part. When the strut is subjected to compression, excessive clearances between all portions of the fitting are conducive to misalinement, and this may result in eccentric loading of the strut. This condition is aggravated if T is relatively small.

RECOMMENDATION

The radius R should be increased. The fitting should be redesigned to incorporate a greater-thickness T. Close tolerances should be used between all mating portions of the fitting, including the bolts.

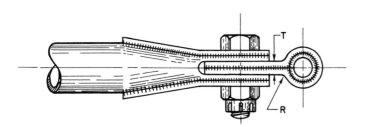

T

R

Welded Joint in a Wing Structure

DESIGN DEFICIENCY

The welded joint is too complicated. It is comprised of 9 tubes intersecting at acute angles, together with approximately 6 gussets and 2 clamps. The assembly is heat-treated subsequent to the welding. It will be noted that welded repairs in the field will be difficult because a reheat-treatment of the welded repair is not practicable. Frequency of inspection in the field is necessarily high to detect incipient failures. This joint is one of two inboard attachment points of a monospar wing panel, and failure of a single chord

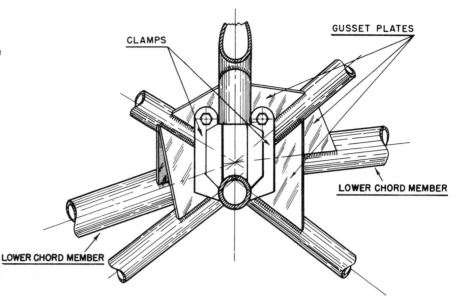

or web member may result in collapse of the spar. This is typical of statically determinate structures wherein the failure of a single member jeopardizes the integrity of the entire structure.

RECOMMENDATION

Complicated welded joints should be avoided, particularly those which are difficult to repair in the field and which necessitate a high frequency of inspection in order to detect incipient weld failures.

Landing Gear to Wing Spar Attachment Fitting.

DESIGN DEFICIENCY

The side plates adjacent to the spar are relatively thin, they lack bending rigidity, and they are subject to distortion and bending caused by the landing gear loads (applied to both directions along the arrowed line). There exists excessive clearance between the fitting and the corners and bottoms of the spar (probably partly due to shrinkage of the wood), consequently the bottom of the spar cannot render good support to the fitting. In one particular fitting, the welding was uneven and of poor quality due to improper welding technique. Bending-fatigue failures resulted at the locations shown.

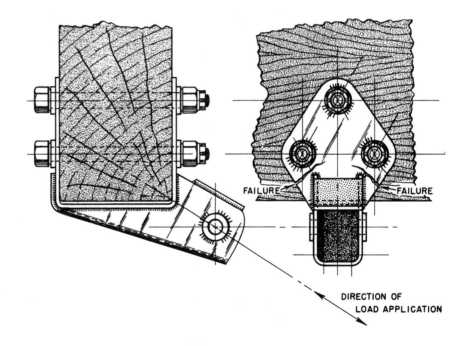

RECOMMENDATION

The fitting should be redesigned to incorporate a more rigid attachment of the side plates to the lower portion of the fitting. A relatively heavy forging appears superior to a sheet metal fitting in this regard.

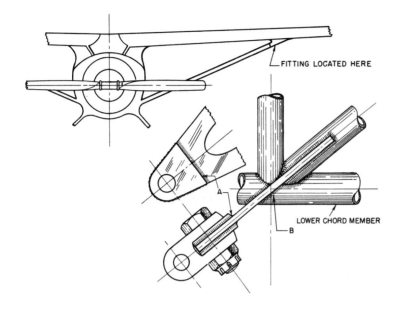

FITTING LOCATED HERE

LOWER CHORD MEMBER

Wing Lift Strut-to-Spar Attachment Fitting.

DESIGN DEFICIENCY

The mass of the main plate is large relative to the washer plates, consequently during welding at *A,* there exists a possibility of burning the washer plates or a cold weld. Another possibility is that the main plate is liable to be weakened due to burning by welding across both its sides at *A.* The lower tubular flange member may be weakened by welding entirely around its periphery at *B.* The fitting as a whole is vulnerable to fatigue failure due to vibration of the lift strut about the flat plate.

RECOMMENDATION

The fitting should be completely redesigned to eliminate welding around the lower chord member and the welding of heavy plate to relatively thin plate, to avoid welding across the main plate which carries the design tension load, and to eliminate bending of the flat plate caused by vibration of the lift strut.

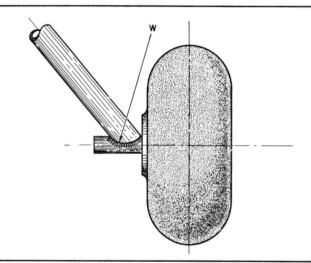

Landing Gear Axle.

DESIGN DEFICIENCY

Landing loads impose a tension load on the weld at *(W)* which, in turn, tends to tear the axle away from the strut at the weld areas. The welds are somewhat vulnerable to repetitive tensile loads.

RECOMMENDATION

The axle-to-strut attachment fittings of the type shown should be reinforced with a welded wrapper plate around the axle and extending up the strut.

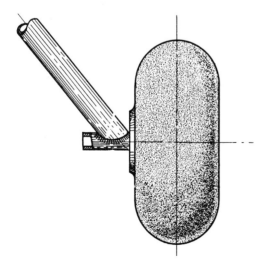

Landing Gear Axle.

DESIGN DEFICIENCY

The welded steel hollow axle was not closed, consequently mud and water collected therein with resultant corrosion and decrease in strength.

RECOMMENDATION

The open end of the axle should be plugged or otherwise closed to preclude the collection of mud and water.

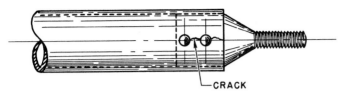

End Fitting for a Push-Pull Tube.

DESIGN DEFICIENCY

The clearance between the inside of the tube and the fitting was excessive. The driving of the rivets caused the tube to be out of round, resulting in critical bending stress in the tube at the rivet holes.

RECOMMENDATION

The inside diameter of the tube end should be reamed or machined and an end fitting with a close-tolerance fit should be installed. In many cases, close-tolerance bolts or taper pins are preferable to rivets. Also, the attaching rivets, pins, or bolts preferably should be spaced 90° apart.

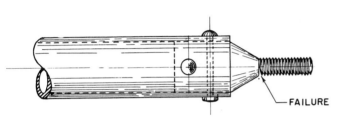

End Fitting for a Push-Pull Tube.

DESIGN DEFICIENCY

The push-pull tube was relatively flexible and of considerable length. The vibration (whipping action) of the push-pull tube induced severe bending in the end fittings, which resulted in their failure due to fatigue.

THE FIX

The diameter of the tube was increased to attain greater rigidity and the threaded portions of the end fittings were increased in size from ¼-28 to ⅜-24.

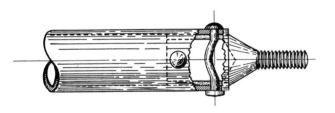

End Fitting for a Push-Pull Tube.

DESIGN DEFICIENCY

The unsupported portion of each rivet is too long and usually the rivet cannot be driven properly. The rivets have an undue tendency to loosen and the joint is of insufficient strength.

RECOMMENDATION

The end fittings should be made solid or recourse should be made to the use of close-tolerance bolts or threaded taper pins. (Maximum unsupported L/D of a rivet should be less than a value of 3.)

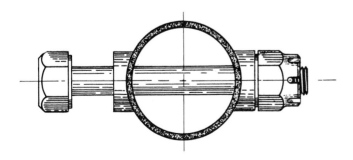

Attachment of an Engine to Its Mount.

DESIGN DEFICIENCY

The engine mount has a tendency to crack due to overtightening the nut.

RECOMMENDATION

A spacer tube should be used to prevent crushing the engine mount tube when the nut is tightened.

Welding Clips / *by Willis L. Cole, Jr.*

I have trouble throwing away anything, and with the high cost of materials today, it becomes a challenge to find uses for scrape material. After making 45 degree cuts on some square steel tubing, I discovered all these little "U-shaped" scraps. My next operation was to make clips from angle extrusion to be welded onto the square tubing (figure 1) and then I recognized the advantage of using these "U-shaped" scraps as clips in place of the angle (figure 2).

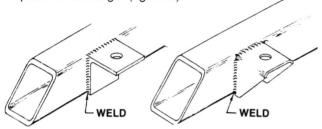

Figure 1 Original Design   **Figure 2 Improved Design**

All the materials to be welded would be of the same thickness, thus it would make welding easier. Also, the U-shaped clips would be stiffer and lighter than the angles (figure 3).

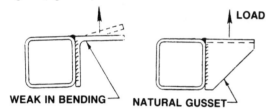

Figure 3 Gusset eliminates bending in part

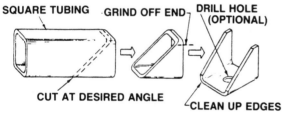

Figure 4 Procedure for making clips

To make additional clips, proceed as shown in figure 4. I chose to drill the hole in the detail part so that I could use the drill-press. If a bolt hole is critical after assembly, then drill the hole after welding.

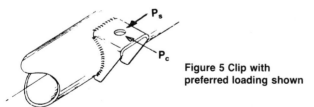

Figure 5 Clip with preferred loading shown

Also, this clip design can be used on round tubing. The important thing to remember is the preferred loading of the clip should be in shear, P_s, and/or in compression, P_c, as shown figure 5, CAUTION - avoid welds in tension.

Shaping Tube Ends on a Metal Lathe / *by Francis H. Spickler*

One of the most important steps toward making a good weld is to produce parts that fit accurately. The writer is using a simple attachment for a metal lathe to shape tube ends to fit other tubes accurately and quickly and at any angle.

The main body of the attachment is made of hard maple 2 in. x 2 in. x 4 in. A ¾ in. x 4½ in. hexagon head machine bolt is turned as shown for a 9 in. South Bend metal lathe, or modified as necessary to fit the lathe available. The small piece of mild steel is fitted to the block and screwed in place in order to keep the block in proper alignment with the compound rest at all times and yet permit easy exchange of blocks for forming any desired size of tubing.

Slide the head of the bolt in the "T" slot on the compound rest and slip the block on the bolt through the 11/16 in. hole. Seat the block so that the piece of mild steel slips into the "T" slot and fasten the block securely with a washer and nut. Place a drill of the desired size tubing in a chuck on the spindle of the lathe and drill a hole through the block. A second hole for a different size tube is also drilled the same way. Remove the block from the lathe and split it in half by sawing on a circular saw and the attachment is completed. As many blocks can be made as desired to prepare for tubing of various sizes. By places the 11/16 in. hole slightly off center a larger hole and a smaller hole can easily be accommodated on one block.

In using the attachment the piece of tubing is clamped in place on the compound rest, the compound rest is set to the desired angle and tightened. A standard reamer with the diameter of the tube against which the shaped tube will butt is mounted between centers of the lathe. Flood the reamer with cutting oil, feed the tube into the turning reamer with the cross feed, and in a matter of moments one has a perfectly fitted pair of tubes.

Fitting tubes on an angle is no problem. One only has to measure the angle of the center line of the tubes on the jig or from an accurate plan, set up the compound rest for the desired angle, and feed the tube into the reamer as it turns. The fit will be better than absolutely necessary with less than a minute spent in making the cut.

To obtain the proper length, cut the raw stock as closely as possible to length, form one end, form the second end being careful to align the tube in the block so that the two ends will be on the proper angle with each other. Next try the tube in the jig. At this point it is easy to measure how much must be removed to achieve the proper length. If the lathe has a graduated cross feed it is a simple matter to remove precisely the required amount. With practice one can usually cut the tube to the proper length so that it fits accurately the first time.

The writer first tried the idea without the mild steel guide block. It worked satisfactorily, but alignment of the tube was tedious, and took more time than forming the tube end. Cutting and fastening this small item saves much time on setting up the tubes for forming.

Carbon steel reamers are satisfactory as long as plenty of cutting oil is used relatively slow speeds. Of course high speed reamers will stand up better.

Be sure to remove all cutting oil before welding in accordance with good welding practice.

A Simple Fuselage Jig

by Frank C. Sabo

This fuselage jig is easy to construct and saves on the amount of wood needed for the job. First thing to do is to check your plans for the length of the fuselage so that you can determine how long to make the jig. I used two 2 x 6 pieces of pine 14 ft. long for my jig. Next I obtained some ⅝ in. plywood and cut strips 8 in. wide and as long as the needed width of the fuse-lage with extra space to spare. These are nailed to the 2 x 6's starting about 3 in. from one end so that when you come to join the two halves of the fuselage you will hav room to tack weld the front cross tube in place (see Fig. 1). The pieces are spaced according to the

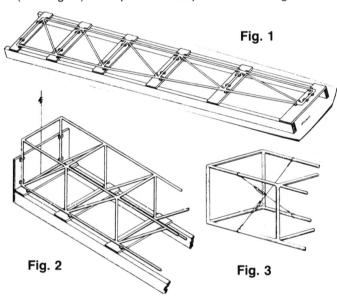

Fig. 1

Fig. 2

Fig. 3

distance of the cross members of the fuselage as shown. Place on two saw horses and level and you're ready to use the jig.

By using plywood cut into narrow pieces, only half the material usually used is required. I used white pine blocks 1½ in. by 2 in. by ¾ in. thick to hold the tubing in place for tack welding. For the cutting and fitting of tubing refer to the Amateur Builders Manual.

Upon completion of the two sides of the fuselage, the jig can be used to hold the sides upright while tacking the top and bottom cross pieces into place, also all diagonals. Square off the ends of the 2 x 6's and nail a piece of ⅝ in. plywood on the end so that it will come up about two-thirds of the way on the front of the fuselage (see Fig. 2). Next use a square to make a center line vertically on the plywood, and then take a string to run a center line the full length of the jig.

You will do all of your measuring for the tubes from this point. Nail blocks to hold up the sides as shown. Remember to always work from the center line — take half of the diameter of the tube you are using and mark on each side of the center of a tube so you will know where the blocks are to be nailed.

Try to keep the fuselage as square as possible during tacking. I used small turn-buckles and wire as shown in Fig. 3 to keep my fuselage square while working on it. Wrap wire around the longeron and into one eye of the turnbuckle, and another wire from the opposite diagonal into the other eye. Take up on the turnbuckle to line up the fuselage. By forming the X close to the clusters it is easier to square up each bay as you weld up the fuselage. I used this in tack welding also.

Welding Tips

Tubular Structures

A welded tubular structure will have terrific stresses set up by the welding, if preventive measures are not taken. When welding two members of a tee joint, as shown in Figure 1, tube (A) tends to draw up. This is due to the fact that most of the expansion is taken care of in the molten metal, but as the weld cools, the base metal contracts beyond its original shape. A whole structure may be distorted as shown in Fig. 2, by the

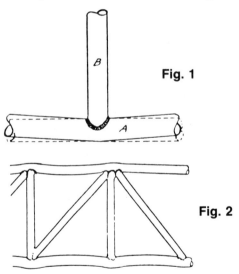

Fig. 1

Fig. 2

contraction in the metal around the joints. Normalizing will relieve most of the stresses, but cannot restore the shape. This will have to be done by hammering out the distorted portions with a mallet. Extreme care must be taken when straightening bent tubing to avoid flattening the tubing.

Buckling can be relieved by pre-heating before the welding begins. Small pieces may be carefully pre-heated with the torch, whereas larger pieces may require heating in a furnace. Contraction still takes place at the weld, but there is also shrinking in the rest of the structure at approximately the same rate. Internal stress at the weld is thereby relieved.

Fig. 3

ROSETTES

Rosettes

Rosettes are often added to a telescoped splice to increase the shear strength of a repaired member. Holes of a pre-determined size are drilled in a staggered formation around the outer tube. Holes for rosettes should have a diameter equal to 1/4 of the tube diameter, but not less than 1/4". The rosette is welded around the inner edge of the hole into the smaller telescoped tube.

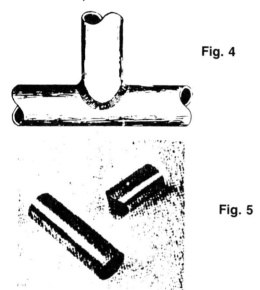

Fig. 4

Fig. 5

Tee and Cluster Joints

Joints in which two tubes meet at an angle are quite common in aircraft construction. The simplest and most frequently used joint is the tee joint, shown in Figure 4. It usually consists of an auxiliary member welded at right angles to a main or continuous member. If the two members join at an angle other than 90 degrees, they constitute a *saddle joint*. Proper construction of the tee joint involves only a small amount of fitting. This fitting can be done by filing the end of the vertical member to a concave shape, and fitting it over the rounded surface of the horizontal member as shown in Figure 5.

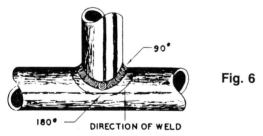

90°

180° — DIRECTION OF WELD

Fig. 6

Welding and Tee Joints

When welding a tee joint as an exercise, the two members should fit very closely so that the edges will not be burned away. However, when a complete damaged member is replaced in a structure, the new member is generally given a maximum clearance of 1/32" at each end for expansion. The tee joint is tacked at four equally distant points after which the tube is welded by the quarter welding method, as shown in Figure 6. As a general rule, these joints are welded from the area of greatest restriction (the sharpest angle) to the area of least restriction.

Where the tube must be welded in a fixed position, as is likely to be the case when airplane structures are repaired, a combination of techniques will probably be employed. At some points on the tubing, the backhand method will give the desired control of the puddle, so that thorough fusion can be obtained. In a restricted area, it may be necessary to "dig in" with the torch to secure penetration to the root of the weld, even though this practice is frowned upon in the welding of flat stock.

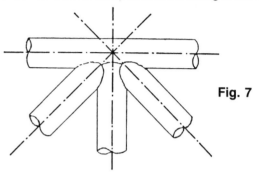

Fig. 7

Cluster Joints

When a number of tubes are welded at a common joint, the joint is referred to as a cluster joint. It is usually composed of a main member, a vertical tube, and other auxiliary tubes at varying angles to the main member. The vertical member is the first one attached. While it may be merely tacked in place, it is usually welded completely because of the additional strength. The other auxiliary members are then carefully fitted into place and welded. In all cluster joints, the center lines of all members usually converge at a common point, as is illustrated in Figure 7. By this precaution, stresses are distributed proportionately upon all members of the joint.

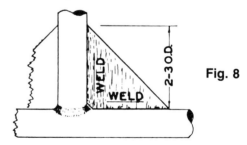

Fig. 8

WELD

WELD

2-3 O.D.

Gussets

Reinforcement plates in the form of flat gussets are often placed between the members of a cluster or tee joint to give added support. See Figure 8. They are usually triangular in shape, with the legs of equal length. The thickness of the gusset should be at least equal to the wall thickness of the tubing. It is usually welded on one side only. In many cases, the gusset does not extend into the apex of the angle but is instead notched out a short distance.

If the unit is heated treated after welding to relieve

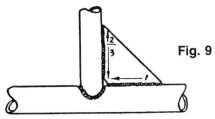

Fig. 9

Fig. 9

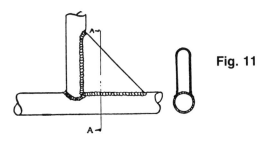

Fig. 11

stresses, the stress concentration is compensated for, and is not as important a factor as the prevention of distortion from contraction. It is then common practice to weld the first edge of the gusset in either direction, since the other edge is free to expand except for the tacks, which are placed near the ends of the seam. Welding of the second edge is completed by beginning at a point about 1/4 to 1/2" in from the outer edge of the gusset, and welding out to the edge; the reminder of the bead is then welded from the point near the outer edge to the inner part of the gusset. See Figure 9. Overlap the parts of the bead about 1/8 - 1/4" to secure thorough fusion. It is not advisable to lift the torch suddenly from the edge of the gusset, as a pinhole is likely to be formed, which may serve as a point for concentration of stresses, leading to failure of the member by cracking. Another recommended practice is to bring the bead around to the end of the gusset, rather than finishing it on the surface of the joint.

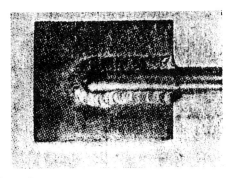

Inserts

A great deal of strength can be obtained from the set up known as the insert, shown in Figure 10. The tubes are slotted and filed to allow a snug fit over the plate which is inserted in the slot. The ends of the tube are filed to a convex shape, then hammered down with a special forming tool. This shaping is done on both sides of the plate. The point at which an engine mount right is welded together is quite often a scarf butt with a plate inserted in the joint to give added strength at this point. Inserts are welded on both sides.

Wrapper Gussets

The wrapper gusset is really a double gusset. It is made up of a square piece of material with side dimensions like those for ordinary gussets. See Figure 11.

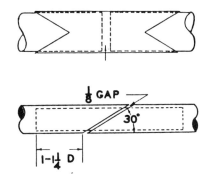

Spacing

As noted in the sketches for the various types of tubing joints and splices, there may be two reasons for spacing the ends of tubing. Spacing may be necessary to allow for expansion, as in the case of the ends of the original tube inside the outer sleeve splice, as is shown in Figure 12, or to allow penetration, as in the case of the ends of the original tube, where an inner splice is used. See Figure 13.

Fusion must extend into the inner sleeve, which cannot be accomplished without space between the ends of the outer members.

Tacking

Tubing is tacked before welding to hold the members in proper alignment and to keep them properly spaced. Tubing is generally tacked at four equidistant points, whether the joint is a tee, saddle, tube to plate, scarf, or fishmouth. Tacks should be light but effective. This tacking at four points is known as quarter tacking.

How to Bend Tubing

by Bob Whittier

The necessary skill to create a smooth bend in a metal tube has proven to be rather elusive, especially for firsttime builders. Often we note a wingtip bow or a tail surface that has grown "lumps" because the builder was unaware of the proper method to make the bend. In the following article by Bob Whittier, most of the tricks of the trade are discussed in detail with added pictures and drawings. Thoroughly read Bob's article until you feel comfortable making your first bend in a piece of tubing. Your finished bird will look better for it! . . .

By the time an amateur aircraft builder completes a project, he will have employed a surprising variety of skills. One of them is tube bending. At first thought this operation might seem like a minor matter — but when one looks into it prior to making a few bends in the tubing of one's small airplane, it is quickly discovered to be a distinct and sizeable branch of the science of metal-working, with its own special tools and techniques.

Seldom does one find a comprehensive digest of tube bending facts in one text, so diverse is the subject. This article, therefore, has been prepared to make available to the aircraft constructor a useful compilation of tube bending information.

Just as various species and thicknesses of wood pose different sawing problems, different kinds and sizes of tubing require specialized bending equipment and methods. Steel tubing of varying diameter and wall thickness must be bent flawlessly for such parts as radial engine mounting rings and tail surface outlines, and perhaps with less fussiness for such nonstructural and concealed parts as exhaust pipes and seat frames. Copper tubing for oil and fuel lines must be bent without flattening, for that restricts flow, causing possible inter-

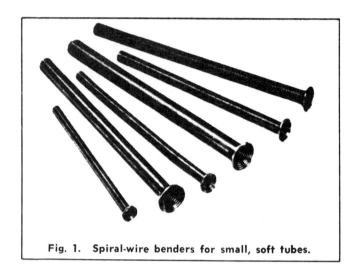

Fig. 1. Spiral-wire benders for small, soft tubes.

ference with engine operation. Aluminum tubing for instrument and hydraulic lines must be bent without weakening or cracking. It doesn't take long to discover that what works admirably for one job or metal will not work well at all for some other task.

Whatever the material or dimensions of a tube, uncontrolled bending leads to flattening on the outside and wrinkling or buckling on the inside of the bend. All bending methods thus share the common purpose of eliminating or limiting such deformation, as well as making possible workmanlike smoothness and uniformity of bends. Similar tubes and those of softer metals can quite readily be bent with hand power, but as size and stiffness increase the use of leverage and power is required. Hence there is a wide range of bending equipment.

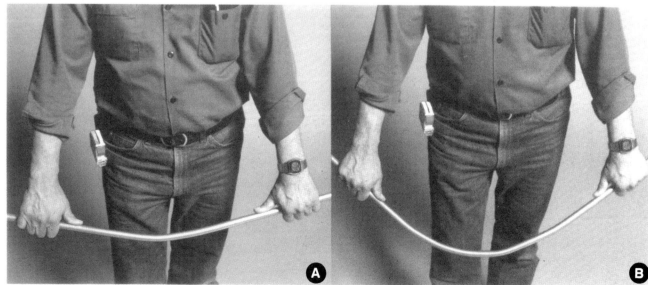

Work bends into tubing by hand gradually.

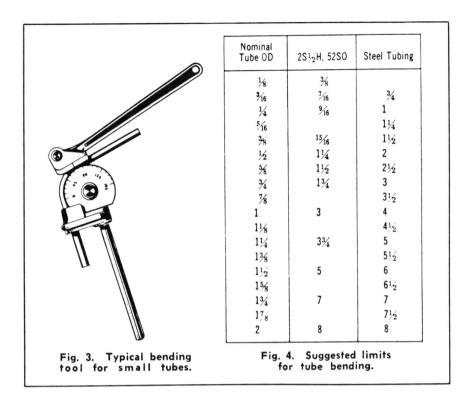

Nominal Tube OD	2S½H, 52SO	Steel Tubing
⅛	⅜	
3/16	7/16	¾
¼	9/16	1
5/16		1¼
⅜	15/16	1½
½	1¼	2
⅝	1½	2½
¾	1¾	3
⅞		3½
1	3	4
1⅛		4½
1¼	3¾	5
1⅜		5½
1½	5	6
1⅝		6½
1¾	7	7
1⅞		7½
2	8	8

Fig. 3. Typical bending tool for small tubes.

Fig. 4. Suggested limits for tube bending.

Considering first the simplest and easiest bends, copper tubing up to about one-quarter inch diameter can readily be hand bent. **A significant reason why is that its wall thickness is rather great in relation to tube diameter. In all tube bending work it is important to remember that as wall thickness decreases, the likelihood of flattening increases.**

The correct way to hand-bend small tubing is shown in Photos A and B. Begin with the hands far apart and work in a gentle bend. Gradually move the hands closer together as the bend is worked sharper. This avoids sudden application of compression on tube walls at the inside of the bend and buckling is minimized.

As diameter goes above about a quarter of an inch, the tendency of copper and other soft tubing is to buckle. To prevent this, use is made of coil springs such as in Fig. 1. Flattening of the tubing in one direction is accompanied by swelling in the other, and the coils surrounding a tube constrain the walls against swelling, thereby discouraging flattening and buckling. Usually slipped over the outside of tubing, they can also be used internally when bends are close to the ends of a longer tube. The bell-shaped ends make it easy to feed tubing into these benders, and twisting combined with pushing tends to screw and slide them off after bending. But, don't twist such a bender so hard against its spiral that the coils are damaged by unwinding. It is possible to make rather sharp bends with their aid.

Before bending, copper tubing should be annealed by heating with a torch until "peacock" colors start playing on its surface, then plunging it into cold water. Don't try to anneal a long piece section by section because irregular hardness will result and make it difficult to obtain uniform bends. Instead, if a long piece can't be dipped, just allow it to cool in the air. Annealing

also makes copper tubes less liable to crack from vibration and could very well be done to old tubes during overhaul.

From about one-quarter inch diameter up, depending on bend radius, it becomes increasingly hard to make neat bends with the bare hands. A selection of tube bending tools is on the market, similar to that in Fig. 3. Models are available to handle tubing up to about 3/4 inch diameter. Since each is accompanied by its own instruction sheet, we will not go into how-to-use detail here. These tools, as well as the coil spring benders, can be used to bend copper, aluminum and dural tubing, but steel is too stiff.

Soft, pure aluminum tubing is all right for instrument lines, ductwork, and other low and medium pressure jobs, but as pressure and tube diameter increase it is important for reliability to use dural alloy tubing of greater strength. Soft aluminum is readily bent, but as all airmen know, aluminum alloys can be quite hard and springy. In production work, factories order their dural tubing in dead soft annealed condition and the amateur should follow this example where possible. Long pieces really should be annealed in a furance so they can be uniformly heated to the correct temperature. Where reliability is at stake in an amateur-built airplane, it would be wise to cut out the section requiring to be bent, anneal and bend it, and re-install it with suitable fittings.

To anneal dural in the shop when it is not possible to use a furnace, play a torch flame over it until a bit of wood held to it will char (aluminum does not change color when heated as does steel and copper so it is easy to reach the melting point — where it will collapse without warning). Then allow it to cool slowly. When using a welding torch, some mechanics use an acetylene flame to coat aluminum with soot to slow

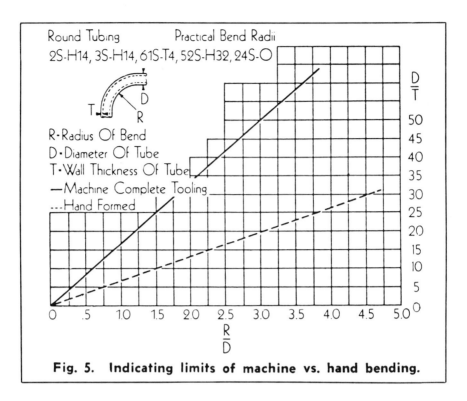

Fig. 5. Indicating limits of machine vs. hand bending.

down the rate of cooling. This aids the annealing process.

As has been intimated, the sharper the bend, the greater the likelihood of flattening and buckling. It is always easier to get a good bend in thick-wall pipe than in thin-wall tubing of the same outside diameter. The table in Figure 4 gives bend radii which have been found to be practical — but, of course, the further one stays from these limits the better. When working on your dream airplane design, remember that good bends cannot be obtained as easily by hand as they can with the production machinery in a factory or at one of the tube-bending plants which do volume subcontracting for manufacturers. The dashed line in Fig. 5 suggests the limits of hand bending compared to machine bending.

While not related too directly to the tube bending, an important point in tube layout design and fabrication is illustrated in Fig. 6. It is not possible to cut and swage tubes so accurately that when a straight one is secured there will be no pull on the tube and fittings. In addition, it is also important to allow for expansion and contraction of tubing with changing temperature, and to allow some bends to absorb vibration and airframe flexing. The methods in the lower two sketches of Figure 6 are therefore correct.

When a long length of tubing must be routed inside a wing or similar structure, obtain some soft iron wire and run it where the tube is to go, bending to fit. Then use it as a pattern to bend the tube without hard-to-correct errors. Copper and small aluminum tubing often come in coil form: beat and roll it on a smooth bench with a block of wood to straighten neatly.

The problem of buckling in light-gauge tubing is so common that much thought has been put into finding solutions. Production tube benders utilize flexible man-

drels, somewhat resembling a number of rollers strung like beads. Pushed inside tubing before bending, they maintain the original cross sectional shape. In limited quantity work and where tubes are to be bent to non-uniform radii, it is common to fill tubing with some solid material such as sand, resin, salt or a special, re-usable bending alloy. To bend with sand, plug one end of the tube tightly with wood and pour in dry, well-sifted, clean sand. Rap the tube as the sand goes in to settle it firmly, and drive a plug in the other end making sure there is no space between sand and plug. It is said to be difficult to pack sand tightly enough to give firm support to thin tubing walls, and another source of trouble is the fact that as the tube bends, it will stretch enough to slack off some and pressure at the bend.

Common table salt is a useful substitute for sand, for it is dry, of uniformly fine texture, is very readily available, and all traces can be flushed out with water after bending. Rosin is good for the cold bending of soft tubing but should not be used for work requiring heating. If you held a torch to the end of a tube, rosin would melt out, and if you put the torch to the center of a rosin-filled tube you might get an explosion! Hardware and paint stores sell it in small retail packages, and chemical and industrial supply firms sell it in bulk containers. Commercial grades are good enough for tube work. Rosin will melt at between 300 and 350 degrees F. and because it is inflammable, melting is done with steam coils or in a closed pot on top of a stove — never with an open flame. It can be re-used if not subjected to temperatures over 600 degrees F. Details on its use, and also much data on the subject of tube bending in general, are given in the booklet, *Copper and Brass Pipe and Tube Bending Handbook* available from Copper and Brass Research Associates, 420 Lexington Avenue, New York, NY 10017.

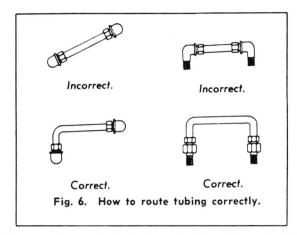

Fig. 6. How to route tubing correctly.

tube pick up some of the alloy's metal, thus changing the tube's own metallurgical makeup.

Coming now to the important subject of bending aircraft steel tubing, we might point out that the popular notion of how it is done is erroneous. If one fills a tube with sand and heats it with a welding torch at the point of bending, the localized heating on the inside of the bend just encourages buckling. If the outside only is heated, when it stretches it can crack or stretch too thin. It usually results in bends of the most unhandsome irregularity, too!

If the finished job is to have that much-desired professional touch the design must be planned in the beginning to fit the available bending methods. If the

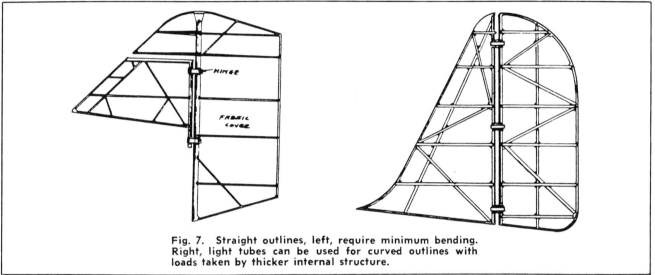

Fig. 7. Straight outlines, left, require minimum bending. Right, light tubes can be used for curved outlines with loads taken by thicker internal structure.

Lead, though soft and readily bent, is not a good bending filler because it shrinks when solidifying and so does not give full support. It also tins the insides of some tubing. Based mainly on bismuth with small amounts of tin and lead added, proprietary bending alloys are sold under such names as Cerrobend or Wood's Metal and Bend Alloy. They melt at temperatures as low as 160 degrees F. and upon solidifying exhibit a slight and useful amount of expansion.

Prior to pouring such an alloy, the inside of a tube is swabbed clean and then slushed with SAE 10 non-additive motor oil to prevent the alloy from clinging to the tube wall. One end is tightly plugged and the tube set at an angle of about 45 degrees. Boiling water is poured in to make the tubing so warm that none of the alloy will cool and stick to its surface. As melted alloy runs in, it pushes the water out. The angle makes the alloy run down one side of the tube so that air pockets do not form. As soon as the tube is full it is set into a tank of cold water, open end up. This quick cooling develops a fine crystalline grain structure in the alloy; if cooling is gradual it hardens with a crack-prone coarse grain structure. When thoroughly cooled, bending is done on a machine or forming block — cold — of course. Afterward the alloy is melted out by immersing the tube in hot water. Never use a torch to heat a tube full of bending alloy as the heat could make the

fin and rudder outline of some factory-built plane is taken as a model, it's important to consider the tube sizes involved when borrowing the nice curves. Sometimes the factory's long experience has led to the de-

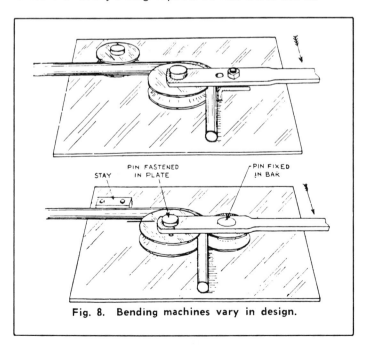

Fig. 8. Bending machines vary in design.

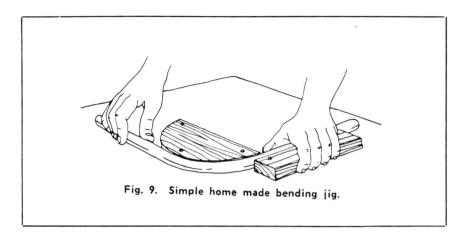

Fig. 9. Simple home made bending jig.

velopment of a bending method that does an otherwise tricky job with deceptive ease. Imitate with caution!

In most fabric-covered light planes the rudder and elevator trailing edge tubes are structural members and as such are of a fairly stiff size of tubing. In some cases it may be wise to use predominantly straight lines as in the left-handed sketch of Fig. 7. Remember, too, that the curve on the top of the rudder could be formed with a carved wood block affixed to the top of the rudder structure, thus eliminating all tube bending work. White cedar, sugar pine and hard balsa are some woods that could be used, making the tips just as in a model airplane. Very often when one inspects an airplane having much curvature in its tail surface outline, it is found that the surface consists of light steel and tubing ribwork and outline members supported by an internal structure which handles the prime loads as in the right sketch of Fig. 7. Naturally, in proportion to tail size the outline tubes are small and rather more easily bent. Remember, for a given wall thickness such as the popular .035 inch, the walls of a small tube are relatively thicker and flattening and wrinkles are less of a problem.

Common mechanical bending machines can make bends of uniform radius only. It is worth knowing that they operate in different ways, for one can use the principles in cobbling up homemade bending machines from boiler plate, planks, angle iron, pipe and even sheaves salvaged from old rigger's pulleys. In Fig. 8, top, the tube is gripped by the lever and is pulled around the large form while at the same time causing the smaller sheave to rotate as the tube moves past it. But in Fig. 8, bottom, the tube does not move and the roller on the bending lever rotates as bending progresses. In these ways the work is done with less effort and fewer scratches on the tubing. On many commercial bending machines and forms, the forms and sheaves are grooved to fit the tubing closely and often the flanges are a little higher than half tube diameter so that they tend to prevent the bulging out of tube walls which occurs simultaneously with flattening.

Such equipment can be approximated in a simple way with a rig such as shown in Figure 9. For a few bends, the face of the hardwood block can be flat, but when several bends are to be made greater uniformity will result if the face is grooved to fit the tubing.

Naturally, torch heating would cause burning of the wood block, and even when a metal one is used the flame could not be played on the inside of the bend. When played only on the outside it will cause cracking

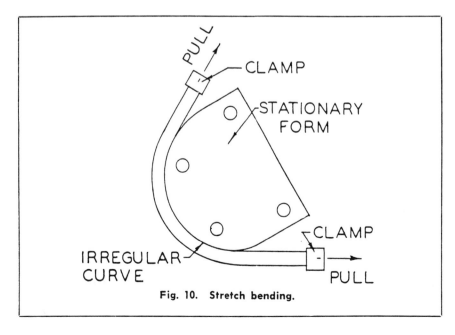

PULL

CLAMP

STATIONARY FORM

CLAMP

PULL

IRREGULAR CURVE

Fig. 10. Stretch bending.

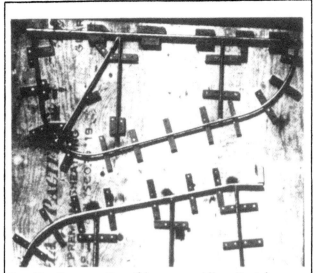

Fig. 11. Among other things, a welding jig takes care of tubing spring-back. Smith Miniplane tail by Mo Malone.

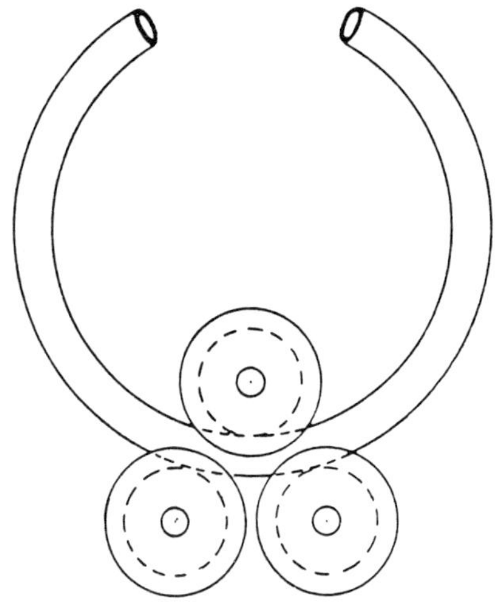

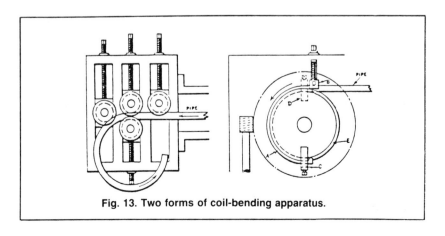

Fig. 12. Principle used to bend tube into rings.

and stretching — with no heating on the inside, there is no compression there to help balance the stretching on the outside, so outside stretching is greater. Heating really works well only when it is possible to heat the tube uniformly in a hearth or furance and then put it onto a bender quickly. A technique called "stretch bending," Figure 10, can be especially useful when such heating is possible.

Actually it is best to use cold bending for light tubing such as is used for tail surface outlines, for this eliminates all problems of irregular heating and local kinking. One EAA member, "Mo" Malone of Lansing, MI, reported good results with a plywood form wherein each corner of the panel is cut to one of the radii found in the tail outline, and U clips are bolted to the edge to hold the tube ends. The center is cut out so the whole rig can be held firmly in vise jaws.

When bends are to be irregular, another technique is useful. Suitably shaped, pressure-distributing wood blocks are made and set up on a table, and the tube filled with sand or bending metal. It is then bent bit by bit using the leverage of its own length and checking often against a cardboard template. Although a bend might look perfect from the side, when tail group members are involved good workmanship also demands

that the tubes appear straight when seen from the leading and trailing edges. So bending on a flat surface like a table helps maintain flatness while bending.

A common problem when using forms and machine is spring-back, and this kind of bending table helps overcome it as one works along the bend — you don't bend to form from which there is spring-back, but from a template, and work extra bend into the tubing while progressing to allow for the spring-back and maintain the desired shape. A rough rule is that when springy tubing is being worked, it should be bent 10 percent more than the final bend so it will be close to what is desired when it springs back.

In light airplane work, probably the best way to take care of spring-back is to use a welding jib such as in Figure 11. Besides holding the members in place for welding and minimizing warpage, it also holds slightly misbent tubing in place until it can be welded up and its spring-back done away with.

Many a mechanic who has tried his hand at the unfamiliar job of bending steel has looked with wonder at the mounting ring of a radial engine and wondered at the perfect circular bending job it represents. It's partly the result of using a filler, partly the result of the control afforded by sturdy commercial bending

Fig. 13. Two forms of coil-bending apparatus.

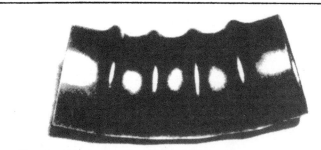

Fig. 14. Wrinkle bending is useful for large tubes. Here, four 10 degree bends give an overall bend of 40 degrees. Tip of welding torch flame is played in arcs to make each wrinkle in turn.

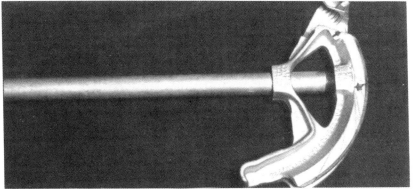

Photo by Jim Koepnick

Tube bending tool used by electricians to bend conduit in nice, even, bends.

machines, and partly the result of the basic method which is the use of rollers as in Fig. 12. In actual practice, some circular and coil benders have four rollers as at the left in Figure 13 to guide the bent tube clear of the machine in spiral fashion. Other coil benders make use of a rotating grooved drum as shown in Figure 13. A length of tubing is fed into the bender and comes out as a coil, which is cut through at each 360 degree mark, the ends pulled together and welded to make the desired engine mount ring or control wheel rim.

One of the most common steel tube bending jobs confronting builders of small planes and restorers of antiques is the fabrication of exhaust pipe elbows. Here the "wrinkle bending" technique can be useful. As all the wrinkles are on the inside of the bend, tube diameter and hence capacity is not decreased, and the tendency of fluids to hug the outside of a bend means that the wrinkles increase flow resistance negligibly, if at all. The same method might help duplicate a tail wheel fork, for metal thickness is not reduced at any point so strength could be maintained, if not increased.

In general, from 7 to 15 degrees may be allowed for each wrinkle, with 10 degrees of bend per wrinkle being a fair average. For tubing between about one and two inches diameter, get two steel plate blanks about 4 inches by 4 inches by 1/4 inch and bore holes in their centers of the same diameter. Saw the squares in half. This gives collars which can be clamped around the tubing to confine torch heat in a narrow band where the wrinkle is to be. Play the torch back and forth across the tube. As the metal softens, the pressure will

be felt to slack off. By skillfully plying the torch and applying more pressure, the wrinkle can be worked in. Use a bubble protractor clipped to part of the tubing to measure each 7, 10 or 15 degree bend to get the several bends uniform.

Well, that's it. Sorry, but we can't include instructions here on how to make a bender!

Welding Cluster Joints

by Jim Frost

When building a Stits Playboy trouble was encountered in doing a good job on some of the cluster joints in the steel tube fuselage. Due to the thin walls of the tubing, it was essential to use a small torch tip, otherwise the tubing would burn through quickly. However, the comparatively large amount of metal at the cluster was able to draw heat away from the weld so fast that good penetration and a smooth head was hard ot achieve. A common blow torch was used and set up so that its flame would play onto the cluster joint as a whole, keeping the metal mass at a uniform high temperature. Then the small tip on the welding torch was able to melt the metal at the actual joint easily, but without burning through the tubing.

Welding Tips / *by Antoni Bingelis*

Although 4130 STEEL (chrome molybdenum or "chrome-moly") is very tough and strong when cold, it is even weaker than mild steel in the heated condition; therefore, it must not be stressed or shocked while in a white-hot state. The following guidelines should be heeded if problems are to be avoided:

1. Do your welding in a draft-free area, otherwise the metal will chill too fast and thereby be weakened.
2. Never use tightly clamped jigs. Spring-type clamps are just fine for holding parts to be welded, and they come in various sizes.
3. Good welders say that starting welding on an edge is not a good technique. Rather, it is best to start at a point away from the edge and work to it. **Caution** — heat builds up fast near the easily heated edges and it is very, very easy to inadvertently burn through the edge of the metal. Watch it and draw the flame away slightly as needed when the edge itself is reached. If you do ruin a piece, make it over. That's where the educational part of homebuilding comes in.
4. In all cases where parts have been tack-welded together, it is most important that you melt completely through the tack as you complete the final weld.
5. As the thickness of the proper tip and the adjustment of the gases becomes very important. Thin metals are easily buckled when too much heat is used.
6. Especially on thin metal and thin-wall tubing, care needs to be taken to clean any dirt, scale, or oxide from the parts to be welded. Percentagewise, as the parent metal becomes thinner, the chances of having dirty metal in the weld in increased. Take time to clean the weld areas.
7. Get in the habit of preheating the metal in the area to be welded.
8. Don't clamp your work in the vise and then try to weld on the part near the jaws of the vise as the heavy metal of the vise will draw away the heat and you'll have difficulty getting the metal hot enough to do good work. Remember, any large or heavy metal areas near the weld areas of work will draw away the heat from the joint and will require a larger flame, thereby increasing the risk of burning the adjacent metal.
9. Be sure your line of weld in the parent metal is heated to proper melting point. Try to keep the weld pool size as uniform as possible.
10. Heat the filler rod to the same melting point before introducing it into the melted pool of metal.
11. Add filler rod as evenly and steadily as possible.
12. Don't rush! Be sure that the added metal and parent metal are puddled together properly.
13. Keep playing the outer envelope flame over the pool to protect it from the oxidizing effect of the air.
14. Melt a certain portion of the parent metal on both sides for the entire length of the weld.
15. Avoid reheating of weld metal which has cooled.

Jig for Holding Hinge Tubing

by James H. Campell

There are numerous little items overlooked by the average person when building an airplane, such as the hinges on the tail surfaces and the little pieces of tubing forming them. When I was putting the hinges on the tail surfaces of my Model D Baby Ace, I ran into the problem of properly aligning the tubes for the hinges and a way to be certain they would be in the center of the leading and trailing edges of the tail surfaces.

The tubing used for the hinges of my particular bird are $3/8$ x .065 x $7/8$ in. 4130. When laying out the tail surface jigs I made the gap between the leading edge

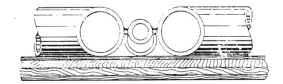

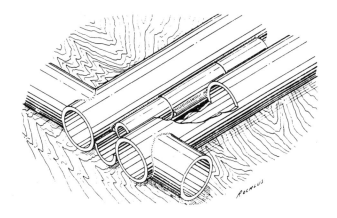

and the trailing edge of the respective tail surfaces to be $1/2$ in. This was to let me use the idea of aligning hinges and getting the hinges properly centered on the tube edges.

I selected a piece of .049 x $1/2$ in. tubing approximately 3 in. long, then cut and ground it down as shown in the accompanying drawing. Mount this tube section between the leading and trailing edges of the tail surfaces as shown. This will allow the $3/8$ in. hinge tube to be held right in the center of the gap, with a ledge on each side for laying a piece of 1/16 in. weld rod for a filler.

Protrude a $1/4$ in. bolt through the hinge stock, and apply the torch and welding rod to the hinges and respective bearers. Remove the jig fixture to the next location and repeat the process. This will give you perfectly aligned hinges and no zig-zag pattern for prospective eyeball engineers to criticize.

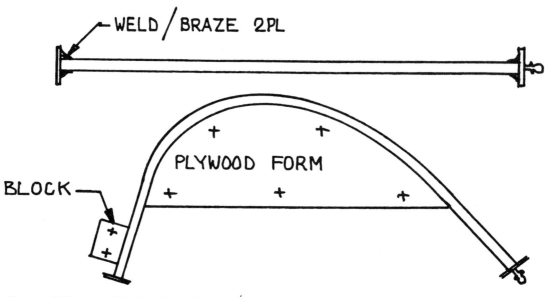

WELD / BRAZE 2PL

PLYWOOD FORM

BLOCK

Bending Thin Wall Tubing / by William N. Kutner

The tried and proven way of forming thin wall tubing is to plug one end, fill with sand or cerro-bend, plug the other end and bend over a form.

The next time you have to form a thin wall tube you may want to try this method. For steel or stainless steel, weld or braze a plate on one end. Make a plug for the other end with a .125 thick material and tap for a zirk grease fitting. Then weld or braze to the tube.

If you are bending cooper or aluminum tubing the ends may be plugged/capped using AN fittings.

Stand tube upright and fill with water to top of tapped hole. Install the zirk fitting and give the assembly about 3 pumps of grease. This will pressurize the water in the tube. The tube must be completely sealed — no leaks.

Now bend over required form. Some change in the form will be required to take care of the spring-back of the tubing.

Editor's Note: Brazing of aircraft parts except by experienced welding engineers is not recommended. Brazing practically always reduces the strength over welding with mild steel rod. There are some processes similar to brazing that are quite strong. The usual use of brazing rod in aircraft welded parts is not recommended in aircraft practice.

Taking the Warp Out of Tubing / by John A. Sons

My welding experience has shown that a common problem in welding steel tube fuselage is that the longerons tend to bow inward when cross pieces and diagonals are welded into place. This is caused by contraction of the longeron metal at the point of the weld, which is of course mostly on one side of the tubing. It seems to shorten the inner side of the longeron, making it bend inward. The cure is to heat the outside of the tubing as shown in the sketch, just enough to soften it and let the tension in the tubing remove the bend automatically. Trial-and-error will show just how much heat to use: just be careful not to let one spot get so hot that movement of the metal causes a ripple or kink.

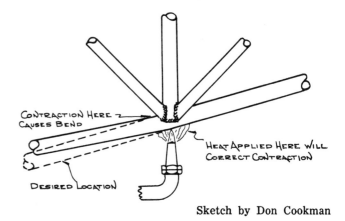

CONTRACTION HERE CAUSES BEND

HEAT APPLIED HERE WILL CORRECT CONTRACTION

DESIRED LOCATION

Sketch by Don Cookman

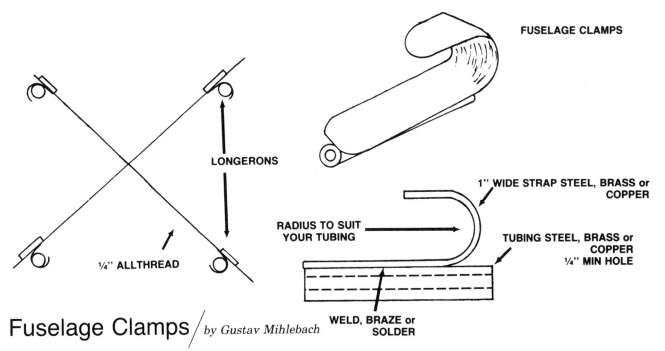

LONGERONS

¼" ALLTHREAD

FUSELAGE CLAMPS

1" WIDE STRAP STEEL, BRASS or COPPER

RADIUS TO SUIT YOUR TUBING

TUBING STEEL, BRASS or COPPER ¼" MIN HOLE

WELD, BRAZE or SOLDER

Fuselage Clamps / *by Gustav Mihlebach*

"I have welded three fuselages (one Hatz and two Pietenpols). While trying to align them for welding I came up with these simple little clamps. I made about 20 of them. They work well and afford very accurate alignment. The fuselage can be squared very easily and you can run a line from the tail post to the firewall. They also don't get in the way when you're welding."

Tack Welding Tips / *by Al Griffin*

Here are some tips I will pass along for what they are worth:

1. I cut 4 inch holes in my plywood fuselage jig at the cluster joints to facilitate tack welding. Also makes nice finger holds for removing frame from jig.

2. Put a piece of paper between two blocks 1 inch by 2 inch by 4 inch. Bore holes through block to match the tube sizes you are using. (¾-⅝-⅜). Remove paper and you have a handy holder for filing and cutting tubing.

3. In laying out my tail feathers I swung the radius on the jig by boring two small holes the correct distance apart in a scrap of aluminum.

4. On the Miniplane compression strut fittings a friend turned mine out on a lathe but if I had to make them again I would construct them as follows: Cut a piece of round stock the I.D. of the compression strut. I'd make it about ¼ inch long, and fabricate to the ¼ inch strap with a countersunk screw or rivet.

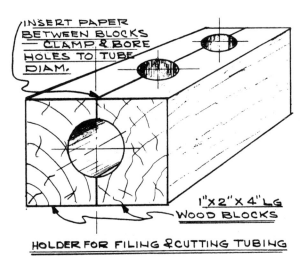

INSERT PAPER BETWEEN BLOCKS — CLAMP & BORE HOLES TO TUBE DIAM.

1"X2"X4" LG WOOD BLOCKS

HOLDER FOR FILING & CUTTING TUBING

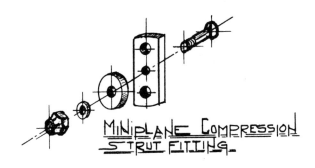

MINIPLANE COMPRESSION STRUT FITTING

Alignment Tool

To aid in aligning two bulkheads or planes during the construction or repair of your aircraft, weld a short piece of tubing on the back sides of several 2 in. C clamps. A piece of threaded rod is then inserted through these tubes and locked in place with flat

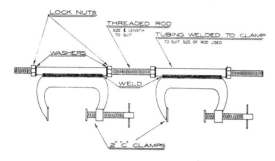

(Drawing by D. E. Browne)

washers and nuts . . . the threaded rod can be as long as required. The clamps can then be adjusted to any width desired.

With three or four such clamping tools, bulkheads, firewalls or engine mounts can be located very accurately.

After numerous attempts to align and space the hinges on my aircraft, this method was employed with little effort:

1. Cut a slot in a ¼ in. dia. tube. Use this as a pin for assembly alignment to prevent hinges binding up after welding.
2. Select two ¼ in. nuts to obtain the desired clearance. Thru-drill to fit snug on split hinge pin and hinge tube assembly.
3. Assemble as per sketch, clamp, align and weld.

by Donald R. Lewis

Bending Steel Tubing

The Fokker DR-1 triplane I am building has many pieces of tubing which are bent into various diameters to form the rudder, cowl ring, etc. I tried to form these by hand, but with little success. Armed with information on bending characteristics of 4130 steel, I then designed and made my "three-ring bender." This thing works so good that no one should be without one.

The triplane rudder has an outline that resembles the top half of a question mark. This piece was bent to perfect shape on the first try in only about five minutes. The piece came out absolutely flawless, with no marks, kinks, or springback. The bender will accommodate up to ¾-inch tubing. It can be made larger if there is such a requirement. The center top wheel is the drive wheel, as indicated by the crank handle. The strap connected to it is the means of adjusting the bending force applied to the drive wheel.

by R. Sands

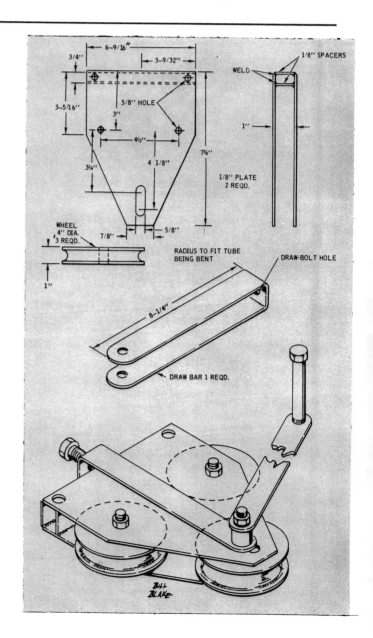

Clamping Tips for Steel Tube Structures / *Tony Bingelis*

Because tubing is round it makes the use of common C-clamps difficult. The clamps will have a persistent tendency to slip off the top center of the tube. A positive cure for this annoying tendency is to use clamps modified as shown in Figure 2. Everyone should have one of these modified clamps . . . two would be better. The concave base brazed or welded to the clamp screw prevents the clamp from slipping off a tube to which it is affixed.

A few homemade bar-like clamps are worth having around the shop as they are easily made. Discount and hardware stores sell threaded rod in various diameters . . . the ¼" size is sufficient for most medium clamping pressures. Being about 3' long and threaded all the way, you have an infinite increments of adjustment for clamping.

All you need is two cross pieces with loose holes drilled in both ends and two of those threaded rods with nuts or wing nuts. These assemble into a very useful clamping device. If you prefer something less cumbersome to manipulate, you could make a few adjustable bar clamps from scrap metal and a few pieces of tubing. Of course, nowadays you can purchase all sorts of clever bar-like clamps . . . if you are willing to pay the price.

As you know, it is often hard to maintain alignment in a welded structure because the heat of welding causes unpredictable degrees of expansion and contraction in each welded cluster. To enable you to maintain a perfect rectangular cross section for a fuselage, you may have to find a way to exert a diagonal pressure (from one longeron diagonally to another) during welding. This is a good place to use a bar clamp or one of the homemade equivalent.

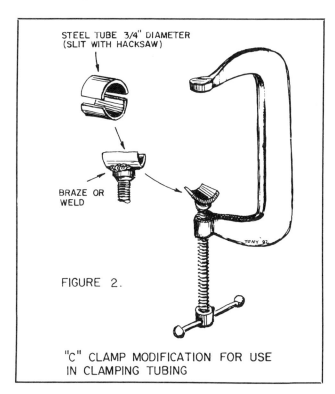

STEEL TUBE 3/4" DIAMETER (SLIT WITH HACKSAW)

BRAZE OR WELD

FIGURE 2.

"C" CLAMP MODIFICATION FOR USE IN CLAMPING TUBING

Welded Fitting Details - Acro Sport

Vertical fin structure.

Note drill rod used for landing gear fitting alignment.

Thoughts on Bending Tubing / *by Roy Clemens*

Everyone uses tubes in one place or another; an aircraft without a tube of some kind is a rarity and most aircraft require tubes to be bent. Bending can be done easily if the proper equipment is available. A professional looking job with very little skill required; however, everyone does not have this equipment so improvision is the next thing.

Small ¼" copper and aluminum can be bent by hand to approximately 2" radius without flattening the tube. Copper should be in its soft annealed state; if not, it can be annealed by heating until soft annealed state; if not, it can be annealed by heating until peacock colors appear on the surface and quench in cold water. Don't try to anneal long sections as hard spots will result making it hard to form uniform bends. Long pieces should be heated as above and allowed to cool in the air. Annealing also makes copper tubes less liable to crack from vibration, and could be done to old tubes during overhaul.

To anneal dural tube in the shop, when it is not possible to have it furnace annealed, play a torce flame over it until a bit of wood held to it will char. (Aluminum will not change when heated.) The allow it to cool slowly; a good coat of soot will slow the cooling process and can be obtained by using an acetylene flame when temperature has been reached.

Copper and aluminum tube comes in coil form. Unroll it on a long bench or board, roll and beat it with a block of wood to straighten it neatly.

Bending larger diameter tubes can cause problems if sharp radius bends are required; on light wall tubing hand bending will cause buckles. A simple jig can be made from wood, mounting a piece of hardwood or plywood cut to the desired radius on the flat work bench and using great skill and patience, work the tube around this die. A lever pivoted at the center of the radius with a grooved roller or piece of hardwood and adjusted so that there is a right fit between the tube and die can be rigged to make a better job and will be will worth the effort if several pieces of the same radius be required. With some work and if metal working tools are available, a very versatile bender can be made for tubes up to one inch as illustrated below:

1. Base or Bench
2. Bending Stop
3. Radius Die
4. Pivoted Roller with Groove
5. Tubing

Of course there is always the filling of the tube with sand or salt or several tube bending low melt alloys which are available. Since sand or salt is the most easily obtained in our area, I will deal with them. Plug one end of the tube by driving in a block of wood, fill with sand or salt, tamping as you fill, then drive a wood plug in the end and proceed to bend the tube using a form tacked to the workbench as a guide. Bend cold. Torch heating would burn the wood and only heat one side of the tube. When heated on one side only it will cause the tube to stretch and crack.

Heating only works well when the whole tube is placed in a furnace and heated uniformly, then quickly taken out and bend around a form. One of the common jobs is the bending of exhaust tubing; here the wrinkle bending method can be used, as all wrinkles are on the inside tube diameter and flow is not decreased to any great degree.

In general, from seven to fifteen degrees may be allowed for each wrinkle . . . ten degrees being common. For tubing between one and two inches in diameter take two plates, 4 inches square by ¼ inch thick, drill a hole in the center the same size as the tubing, saw these across the hole and make collars out of them so they can be clamped around the tube where the wrinkle is to be. This confines the torch heat to a narrow band; by playing the torch back and forth across the tube while applying pressure at the end of the tube, as the metal softens, the pressure will be felt to slacken off and by playing the torch and applying more pressure the wrinkle can be worked in. A bubble protractor clamped to the end of the tube and set the desired angle will be helpful in getting uniform bends.

How the Professionals do it!

● One light airplane factory uses a trick you wouldn't believe if you had not seen it done. They strike longerons with a rubber mallet to bow them out about a quarter of an inch. When dope tightens the fabric, it pulls them in so they are straight rather than bowed in between cluster joints. On fuselages where the longerons are quite thin and long between joints, put fabric on with less than normal tension to prevent dope from pulling it too tight for the good of the longerons. If too much heat is applied to Ceconite it will shrink even more when doped and can even make the structure collapse.

● It is considered good aircraft practice to drill holes slightly undersize in vital fittings and then ream the holes to true and accurate final size. Due to shifting of the work, bending of the drill, variation in grind, increasing dullness with use, etc., twist drills cannot be relied on to make consistently accurate holes. M-M-A, Inc., Lancaster, Pa., makes tap guides sold under the trade name 3-I-Q which hold hand-turned taps at exact right angles to the work and insure true, uniform tapping. When taps go in crooked, they bite a lot of metal from one side of the hole and too little from the other side, giving unreliable threads and causing tap breakage.

● Don't use a scriber to mark steel tubing for cutting; scratches that deep are sure to be starting places for cracks. Get a silver colored pencil of the type used to mark blueprints. It marks steel tubing well, even when oily or greasy, and can be seen even when the metal is heated for tack welding.

● To make the cutting of steel tubing faster and neater try one of the chromeplated tubing cut-off wheels for table saws, available from Sears and power tool dealers. An ordinary plumber's tubing cutter works well, too.

All steel tubing fits should have gaps not over 1/16 in. Slight looseness at the ends of tubes is used to allow for heat expansion and avoid a weld at one end pushing things out of alignment at the far end. But too-large gaps lead to excess use of rod for filling, with weak joints and danger of burning through tube walls.

Cutting Tubing

by Larry and Kenneth Stephens

When we began fitting the pieces for the fuselage of our Acro II, we found it wasn't too difficult to shape each end of a tube, but getting the two ends in proper relation to each other was another matter. We completely eliminated this problem with the simple clamp shown in the photograph. We quickly realized that for the kind of results we wanted, good fit for easier welding and minimum added rod, the clamp was nothing short of miraculous.

To try the idea, we picked up a scrap of 2x4 about 4 inches long, and we stuck with that material for the 6 or 8 clamps we eventually put into use. We drilled a tube diameter hole near one end (through the 2-inch dimension) then belt sanded the end until the hole just broke through. To provide clamping action, we sawed

Sand the end of the block so the tubing just lies flat on the fuselage jig.

One big advantage? The tube won't roll so one end can be cut to fit and the second end is easier to make.

a slot past the hole about 2 inches and cross-drilled a hole for a 1/4 inch bolt about 1 inch above the hole for the tube.

We used the clamps to fit cross tubes for the fuselage in the following manner. Remove one longeron from the jig. Secure a piece of stock in the clamp. (If the cross piece is smaller diameter than the longeron, tape shims on the jig near the longeron and on the bottom of the clamp to line up the centerlines. If the jig is not quite flat, more or less shim will correct the situation so that the clamp doesn't rock.) Fit the first end of the tube to the longeron or cluster. You should find this to be easier and faster than without a clamp, and this is only the beginning.

Now comes a benefit that we had not anticipated. The clamp can easily be used to produce a finished piece which is the correct length, as well as with ends that are for the same airplane. Nail a jig block on the jig so that it touches the back side of the clamp. Remove the longeron and other cross pieces required at the second end. Work on the second end of the piece until the clamp block touches the extra jig block and you will have the correct length. If you want the piece to have some clearance, temporarily attach a shim to the extra jig block before you position it behind the clamp block. Remove the shim before you start fitting the second end.

We also used the clamps on diagonal pieces at transverse stations, but it has been a while, and the details are a little murky. I'm sure a builder who likes the clamp can figure it out.

We got a lot of favorable comments on our fuselage, and I think the excellent fits we were able to achieve with the clamp had a lot to do with that.

Inhibiting Rust on Steel Tube Fuselage

by Ken Spratley

Once the fuselage for my Blue Jay (a sort of personalized PA-12 Super Cruiser) was finished, I decided to corrosion proof the interior of the tubing. First, place the fuselage over a gravel driveway or patch of dirt. I did the job in my back yard and the raw linseed oil killed the grass. General practice says that you drill the main longerons at each cluster internally so that when the hot oil is poured into the tailpost, it can snake its way into the cross tubes and diagonals. Apparently, you are supposed to feel the tubes for warmth to ensure that all tubes are coated. This is what I developed for my airplane: All welding should be completed, even putting on a small bracket after treatment will burn off the oil. Longerons were easy — each was drilled, filled to 1/3 capacity and plugged with a PK screw. I then drilled each individual tube twice with a 5/32nd inch fill hole and a 1/8 inch breather about 1/2 inch from the end. For example, on the sides, all tubes were drilled just above the lower longeron for the top to bottom and was to the right side. Using a syringe from the local drug store, each tube was filled about 1/3. After completion of a side, the fuselage was flipped so the next row of holes was at the top and the process was repeated. The fuselage was elevated from end to end and rotated a number of times for about 20 minutes.

Then it was set on two saw horses with one row of screws at the bottom. As the screws were removed, the oil was caught in a can with newspapers spread under it to catch the drips. In the cases where there is an air lock, the oil can be extracted by using the syringe. After all the oil is out, let the thing stand for a couple of hours, rotate every once in a while to ensure good coverage and complete draining. Then the fuselage is wiped down with varsol.

Normally, drive screws or rivets are placed in the holes, but when this is done, their placement becomes important. If a screw or rivet is against, or even close to the fabric, a hole will develop in time. Each of the oil holes should be deburred and the areas around them cleaned with lacquer thinner. Small postage stamp sized pieces of fiberglass cloth are then cut, enough to cover all the holes with a few spares. Each is glued in place with polyester resin and after drying, a couple more coats are put on and all spots are touched up with zinc chromate. It is almost impossible to see where the holes were drilled, and this method ensures that each and every tube is properly coated, yet there is no residue. The entire job took four hours, and I was feeling my way along. One gallon of linseed oil is more than enough. Every one of my tube components was likewise treated. There is no use spending $15,000-$20,000 and then allowing it to wear away from the inside. You get a much better feeling at 3000 feet knowing that the "rusties" can't get a toe hold!

Protecting Tubing from Rust

by Edward Dyck

Here is an idea of mine that should be of benefit to anyone building a fuselage of chromoly steel tubing.

In building my Christavia MK-1 project, I thought about using linseed oil inside the tubing to protect against rust and then it occurred to me that if I could only get rid of the oxygen inside of the tubing, that would do it also — as well as eliminate the messy job with the linseed oil.

I drilled 1/16 inch holes in the tubing within all the tubing joints and clusters and installed a schrader valve fitting that has a 1/8 inch N.P.T. male thread end on it.

At the front end of the fuselage, visible from the pilot's seat, I welded on a similar pipe fitting into which I threaded a small pressure gauge - 0 to 100 p.s.i.

This now allowed me to pressure test all tubing welds on the entire fuselage assembly using a soap solution. Several leaks were discovered even though all welds appeared perfect to the naked eye. Don't forget to release the air pressure before welding up the leaks.

After all welding is completed on the fuselage I plan to purge out the air from inside the tubing using a bottle of nitrogen and leaving it pressured up to about 50 p.s.i. By using an inert gas such as nitrogren or argon, no rusting should take place in the tubing.

The greatest benefit though will be that if a crack ever develops in the fuselage structure it will be detected by a loss of pressure on the gauge.

To purge the air out from the tubing the following procedure could be used:

Pressure up the tubing with nitrogen, wait a few minutes for the nitrogen to dilute the air inside the tubing, then release the pressure at the gauge fitting at the front. Replace gauge, repeat above procedure a few times and the oxygen level inside the tubing should be practically zero. Finally, leave about 50 p.s.i. of nitrogen pressure on the gauge.

Hinge Alignment / *by Clyde P. Bott*

After numerous attempts to align and space the hinges on my Wittman, this method was employed with little effort:
1. Cut a slot in a ¼ in. dia. tube. Use this as a pin for assembly alignment to prevent hinges binding up after welding.
2. Selection two ¼ in. nuts to obtain the desired clearance. Thru-drill to fit snug on split hinge pin and hinge tube assembly.
3. Assemble as per sketch, clamp, align and weld.

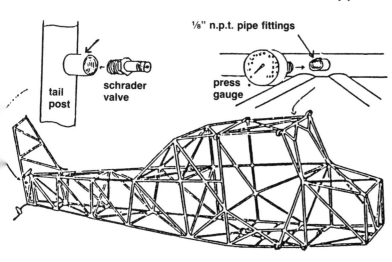

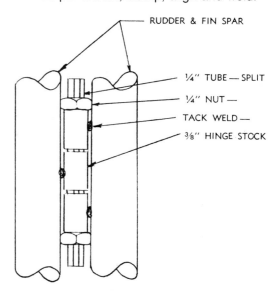

112

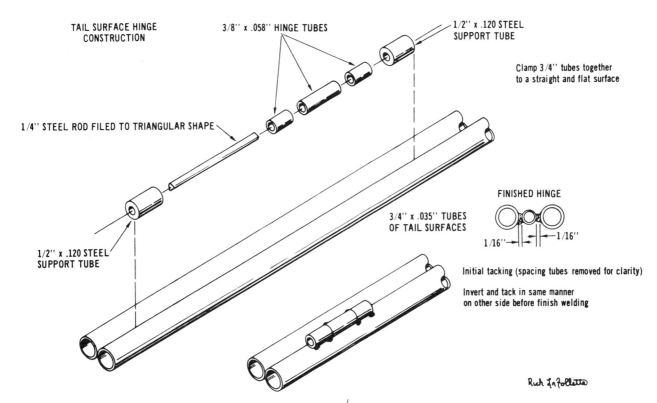

TAIL SURFACE HINGE
CONSTRUCTION

3/8'' x .058'' HINGE TUBES

1/2'' x .120 STEEL
SUPPORT TUBE

Clamp 3/4'' tubes together
to a straight and flat surface

1/4'' STEEL ROD FILED TO TRIANGULAR SHAPE

FINISHED HINGE

3/4'' x .035'' TUBES
OF TAIL SURFACES

1/16''——| |——1/16''

1/2'' x .120 STEEL
SUPPORT TUBE

Initial tacking (spacing tubes removed for clarity)

Invert and tack in same manner
on other side before finish welding

Rich LaFollette

Tail Surface Hinge Construction / *by Mark Yelich*

While working on the tail surfaces of my little bi-plane, I came up with a very simple method of aligning and attaching the hinges to the surfaces.

As can be seen from the sketches, the small pieces of tubing which form the hinges are merely positioned at the desired locations along the two structural tubes. They will align themselves. The 1/2 inch spacer tubes will support the hinge tubes 1/16 inch away from the structure to give clearance for the fabric covering. Each hinge tube is then tack-welded in place as shown. Next, the spacers are removed, the assembly inverted, the spacers repositioned, and this side tacked. Now the tubes can be finish welded.

At this point the two tubes are probably bent in several directions because of stresses at the hinge points. To straighten the tubes, heat the arched side of the tube to a medium-red glow. When it cools it will contract and straighten out. If you can't get good results this way, heat the other side of the tube slightly while the arched side cools. A little patience here, and an eye for straight edges will yield a straight assembly ready to be put into the jig for further assembly.

Be sure to grind or file the 1/4 inch rod to the triangular cross-section shown. This insures easy removal after scale develops inside the hinge tubes.

Welding Table from Barbecue / *by Chet Klier*

This handy and economical welding table can easily be constructed from an ordinary home barbecue. Moist sand is placed in the fire pan and then spread to give an even, smooth surface. The firebrick are then placed on top of sand bed and fitted into place. The bricks are easily shaped with hammer and chisel to fit the round edges of the fire pan. (All bricks should be numbered so that they can be easily replaced after the barbecue has been repossessed for outdoor cooking).

A brazier hood will provide a wind screen and spark shield while welding small fittings. Hot pieces can be placed on the top of the hood to cool after welding. Drawings show details of the welding table.

LEVEL BED OF SAND

FIREBRICK

SECTION A-A

EAA FLIGHT ADVISORS

Volunteers who can provide assistance in successfully getting the builder safely through certification and flight testing

You have completed the aircraft of your dreams. Are you ready to fly it? Are you sure all the paper work is ready to be submitted? Are you knowledgeable of the flight characteristics of your specific aircraft? Are you current in that specific type of aircraft: high performance, conventional gear, ultralight? Do you have a specific test plan put together?

You should be asking these questions of yourself. None of us can have all the answers to all the questions.

An *EAA Flight Advisor* is ready to help you to get in the air as quickly and safely as possible. *EAA Flight Advisors* are individuals who have the experience to help you before your initial flights of amateur-built, light planes, high performance, ultralights and restorations. They are familiar with the resources available to assist you in: initial flight programs, aircraft check-out and biennial flight review requirements.

The success of the amateur-built movement has provided the need for this EAA program that will enhance the safety of the sport aviation community. An *EAA Flight Advisor* will assist you in self-evaluation of builder/pilot current level of proficiency and experience compared to the characteristics of the aircraft.

He or she will counsel the builder in planning a complete ground and flight test program.

It is important for pilots to know what they should be looking for in the initial flights, and have an organized plan to operate the aircraft. We must all be proactive to ensure sport aviation activities unencumbered by additional government regulation.

Resources are available from the government, EAA, kit manufactures and type clubs. An *EAA Flight Advisor* can help you ensure you have all the latest information and provide an extra safety benefit to pilots.

An *EAA Flight Advisor* can help you beat the odds and ensure the successful beginning of your sport aircraft adventure.

If you are completing an aircraft and getting ready to fly, consult an *EAA Flight Advisor*. This is just one more reason why you are an EAA member. Call EAA at 414/426-4800 for more information.

EAA Videos, Manuals and Publications

"How To" Videos to Help You Build

EAA offers a great selection of videos that clearly demonstrate proper techniques of aircraft building, welding, covering and painting.

Aircraft Welding (45 min.)   21-36687
Great introduction for the novice or a refresher for experienced welders. Learn how to run a bead, read a puddle, tack weld, cluster weld and much more!

Building Your Own Airplane: CORROSION (60 min.)   21-38113
Corrosion threatens every aircraft exposed to humid conditions and acid rain. Learn from Geo Hindall how to recognize, prevent and protect your aircraft against corrosion.

Aircraft Painting (60 min.)   21-36467
Join a professional paint crew as they show you the detailed steps and techniques involved when painting an aircraft.

Building Your Own Airplane (40 min.) 21-10429
Answers many of the questions on what project to select, tools and skills required, construction time, documentation, inspection, insurance and other factors to consider when building. Ideal for first time builders.

Fabric Covering With Ray Stits (120 min.) 21-36141
Learn the delicate art of fabric covering from the expert — Ray Stits (EAA #136) — the man who developed the popular Stits Poly-Fiber Aircraft Coating process. Step by step instructions.

Order from:

EAA Catalog Sales
P.O. Box 3065, Oshkosh, WI 54903-3065
Call Toll Free - U.S. & Canada
1-800-843-3612
(or 414-426-4800 — Fax 414-426-4873)
MAJOR CREDIT CARDS ACCEPTED

Aircraft Welding (120 pgs)   21-37864
Fundamental welding techniques for the building & repair of aircraft, from the pages of Sport Aviation and other sources. 120 pages filled with aircraft welding tips and information.

Wood Aircraft Building Techniques (140 pgs) 21-18100
Excellent resource book on "How To" build or repair wood aircraft.

Custom Built Sport Aircraft Handbook (144 pgs) 21-13510
A guide to construction standards for the amateur aircraft builder and detailed information on FAA contact and applicable FARs.

CAM-18 — Aircraft Maintenance Manual (209 pgs) 21-13460
Easy to read guide to maintenance, repair & alteration of aircraft. Includes airframes, powerplants, propellers & appliances. CAM 18 is the early version of AC-43.13, current guideline to repair of type certificated aircraft.

CAM-107 — Aircraft Powerplant Handbook   21-13470
(350 pgs)
C.A.A. Technical Manual for Maintenance and Repair of Aircraft Powerplants.

Firewall Foreward (295 pgs)   21-13950
By Tony Bingelis. Manual on piston engine installations. One of the best engine reference manuals for the amateur builder.

Sportplane Builder (300 pgs)   21-30140
By Tony Bingelis (Vol. I) Aircraft construction methods and techniques for the homebuilder. Articles taken from Tony's columns in Sport Aviation magazine.

Sportplane Construction Techniques (360 pgs) 21-01395
By Tony Bingelis. (Vol. II) More aircraft construction tips for the homebuilder. Articles taken from Tony's columns in Sport Aviation magazine.

Flying and Glider Manuals
Reprints of original "Building and Flying Manuals" published from 1929 to 1933 by Modern Mechanix and Inventions.

1929 Flying & Glider Manual   21-14167
Contains information on flight lessons plus building the Heath Super Parasol, Russell-Henderson Light Monoplane and an easy to build glider.

1930 Flying & Glider Manual   21-14168
Plans for building a Heath Baby Bullet, set of light plane metal floats; building the Northop Glider, Lincoln Biplane, Alco Sportplane, plus other tips on building and welding.

1931 Flying & Glider Manual   21-14169
Building the "Longster", Georgias Special, a glider and secondary glider, Driggs Dart, the Church Midwing, the Heath Seaplane Parasol and its pontoons, the Northop Glider and other gliders.

1932 Flying & Glider Manual   21-14170
Building the Pietenpol Aircamper with Ford motor conversion Powell "P-H" Racer, the Heath Super Soar Glider, Penquin practice plane, Ramsey "flying bathtub" and other kids. Also, build your own hangar.

1993 Flying & Glider Manual   21-14171
Building the Gere Sport Biplane, Pietenpol floats, Pietenpol Sky Scout, and Henderson Longster. Also, Long Harlequin Motor plans, a hydroglider and info on building propellers.

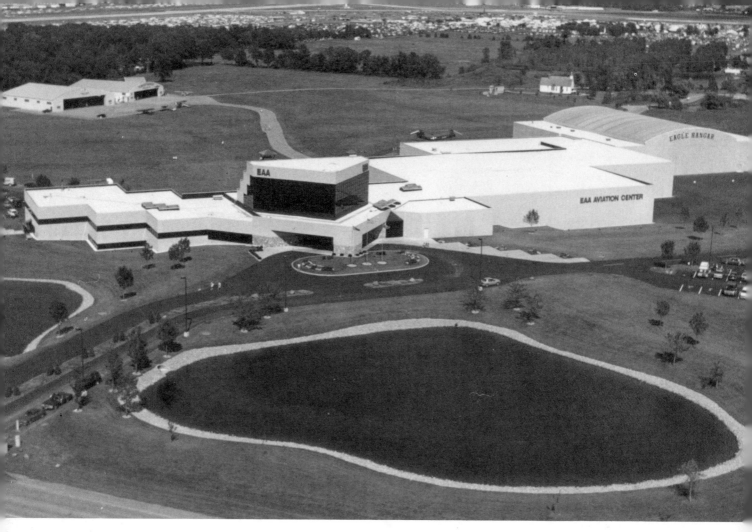

Visit the EAA Air Adventure Museum

Visit the world's largest, most modern sport aviation museum. Over 90 full size aircraft on display many rare, historically significant aircraft. Prototypes of some of sport aviation's most successful designs. See World War I fighters, antiques, classics, and business aircraft of the 30s — racers, experimental and aerobatic aircraft, ultralights and more! See exact replicas of the 1903 Wright "Flyer" and Lindbergh's "Spirit of St. Louis". View the impressive art and photo galleries, historical artifacts, audio-visual presentations and four unique theatres. Enjoy the barnstormer era that comes to life seasonally at the Pioneer Airport adjacent to the museum — and visit the new Eagle Hangar that honors the aviators of World War II and displays many of the famous aircraft flown in combat. Great gift shop too!

Easy to Reach: Located off Hwy 41 at the Hwy 44 exit Oshkosh, WI — adjacent to Wittman Regional Airport.

Museum Hours: Open Monday thru Saturday 8:30 a.m. to 5:00 p.m.
Sunday 11:00 a.m. to 5:00 p.m.

EAA AVIATION FOUNDATION

EAA Aviation Center Oshkosh, WI 54903-3065   414-426-4800